100 MATHS HOMEWORK ACTIVITIES

C000119404

NTENTS

Published by
Scholastic Ltd,
Villiers House,
Clarendon Avenue,
Leamington Spa,
Warwickshire CV32 5PR

© Scholastic Ltd 2001
Text © Suzanne Edwards 2001
Additional material on
pages 6–8 © Ann Montague-Smith 2001
1 2 3 4 5 6 7 8 9 1 2 3 4 5 6 7 8 9 0

AUTHOR
Suzanne Edwards

EDITORIAL & DESIGN
Crystal Presentations Ltd

COVER DESIGN
Joy Monkhouse

ILLUSTRATOR
Peter Smith

Acknowledgements
The publishers wish to thank:
Ann Montague-Smith for her invaluable advice in
the development of this series.
The Controller of HMSO and the DfEE for the use
of extracts from *The National Numeracy Strategy:
Framework for Teaching Mathematics* © March 1999,
Crown Copyright (1999, DfEE, Her Majesty's
Stationery Office).

	100 MATHS HOMEWORK ACTIVITIES YEAR 2		NATIONAL NUMERACY STRATEGY		100 MATHS LESSONS		
PAGE IN THIS BOOK	ACTIVITY NAME	HOMEWORK	STRAND	TOPIC	NNS UNIT	LESSON	PAGE
29	Counting and writing numbers	Practice exercise	Numbers and the number system	Counting and number properties	1	1	23 / 24
30	Counting objects on a tray	Maths to share	Numbers and the number system	Counting and number properties	1	1	23 / 24
31	Counting on in ones	Maths to share	Numbers and the number system	Counting and number properties	1	2	24 / 25
32	Counting on and back in ones	Practice exercise	Numbers and the number system	Counting and number properties	1	3	25 / 26
33	10 game	Maths to share	Calculations	Recall of + and – facts	2 / 4	1	30 / 31
34	Adding two numbers	Investigation	Calculations	Understanding + and –	2 / 4	3	32
35	Tens and units	Practice exercise	Numbers and the number system	Place value and ordering	2 / 4	4	33
36	Doubling numbers	Practice exercise	Calculations	Understanding + and –	2 / 4	6	34 / 35
37	Target 50p	Maths to share	Calculations	Mental calculations + and –	2 / 4	8	36
38	Adding two 'teens' numbers	Practice exercise	Calculations	Understanding + and –	2 / 4	9	37
39	20 game	Maths to share	Calculations	Mental calculations + and –	2 / 4	11 / 12	38 / 39
40	Add and subtract 10	Practice exercise	Calculations	Mental calculations + and –	2 / 4	13	40
41	£1.00 problem	Investigation	Solving problems	Number problems in money	2 / 4	8	36
42	Estimating and measuring length	Maths to share	Solving problems	Number problems in measures	5 / 6	1 / 5	46 / 49
43	Measure up	Maths to share	Solving problems	Number problems in measures	5 / 6	1 / 5	46 / 49
44	Hunt for circles and spheres	Investigation	Measures, shape and space	Shape and space	5 / 6	6 / 8	49 / 50
45	Shapes made from five squares	Games and puzzles	Solving problems	Reasoning about shapes	5 / 6	6 / 8	49 / 50
46	My number/your number games	Maths to share	Numbers and the number system	Counting and number properties	8	1	59 / 60
47	Odd and even dominoes	Investigation	Numbers and the number system	Counting and number properties	8	2	60 / 61
48	Scoring 12 with three cards	Games and puzzles	Calculations	Mental calculations + and –	8	4	62
49	Rounding numbers	Practice exercise	Numbers and the number system	Estimating and rounding	9	1	64 / 65
50	Ordering numbers	Maths to share	Numbers and the number system	Place value and ordering	9	2	65
51	Adding three numbers	Games and puzzles	Calculations	Mental calculations + and –	9	3	66
52	Pay and change from 50p	Practice exercise	Solving problems	Number problems in money	9	5	68
53	Foot work	Maths to share	Calculations	Understanding × and ÷	10 / 11	1	72 / 73

	100 MATHS HOMEWORK ACTIVITIES YEAR 2		NATIONAL NUMERACY STRATEGY		100 MATHS LESSONS		
PAGE IN THIS BOOK	ACTIVITY NAME	HOMEWORK	STRAND	TOPIC	NNS UNIT	LESSON	PAGE
54	Domino multiplication	Practice exercise	Calculations	Understanding × and ÷	10 11	3	73 74
55	Hand work	Maths to share	Calculations	Understanding × and ÷	10 11	2	73
56	£1.00 to spend at the paper shop	Practice exercise	Solving problems	Number problems in money	10 11	7	76
57	Ways to halve a pizza	Games and puzzles	Numbers and the number system	Fractions	10 11	10	78
58	Baking cakes	Maths to share	Measures, shape and space	Measures	12 13	1 3	82 83
59	Ball games	Maths to share	Measures, shape and space	Measures	12 13	5	83 84
60	TV times	Investigation	Solving problems	Organising and using data	12 13	6	84
61	Timing games	Maths to share	Measures, shape and space	Measures	12 13	10	87 88
62	Hunt for cupboards and drawers	Investigation	Solving problems	Organising and using data	12 13	8 9	86 87
63	Counting and writing numbers 99–0	Practice exercise	Numbers and the number system	Counting and number properties	1	3	99
64	Odd and even telephone numbers	Investigation	Numbers and the number system	Counting and number properties	1	2	98
65	Counting in hundreds	Maths to share	Numbers and the number system	Counting and number properties	1	3	99
66	Number squares	Practice exercise	Numbers and the number system	Place value and ordering	2 4	3	104
67	Target 50	Games and puzzles	Numbers and the number system	Place value and ordering	2 4	4	105
68	Change please!	Maths to share	Solving problems	Number problems in money	2 4	5	106
69	Adding two-digit numbers	Practice exercise	Calculations	Recall of + and – facts	2 4	6	106 107
70	Scoring 30 with three cards	Games and puzzles	Solving problems	Number problems in 'real life'	2 4	7	107
71	Sorting and counting cash	Maths to share	Solving problems	Organising and using data	2 4	10	109
72	Adding three two-digit numbers	Investigation	Calculations	Understanding + and –	2 4	11	109 110
73	Pay and receive change from £2.00	Practice exercise	Solving problems	Number problems in money	2 4	14	112
74	A special treat	Maths to share	Solving problems	Number problems in money	2 4	15	112
75	Container hunt	Investigation	Measures, shape and space	Measures	5 6	1 4	115 117
76	Pouring drinks	Maths to share	Solving problems	Number problems in measures	5 6	1 4	115 117
77	Hunt for squares and cubes	Investigation	Measures, shape and space	Shape and space	5 6	5 8	117 118
78	Draw a symmetrical pattern	Practice exercise	Measures, shape and space	Shape and space	5 6	5 8	117 118

PAGE IN THIS BOOK	ACTIVITY NAME	HOMEWORK	STRAND	TOPIC	NNS UNIT	LESSON	PAGE
	100 MATHS HOMEWORK ACTIVITIES YEAR 2		**NATIONAL NUMERACY STRATEGY**		**100 MATHS LESSONS**		
79	Scoop and count	Maths to share	Numbers and the number system	Counting and number properties	8	1	123 / 124
80	Counting on and back 3	Maths to share	Numbers and the number system	Counting and number properties	8	3 / 4	125 / 127
81	Counting in tens targets	Maths to share	Numbers and the number system	Counting and number properties	8	3 / 5	125 / 127
82	100 game	Maths to share	Calculations	Recall of + and – facts	9	1	129 / 130
83	Positioning numbers	Maths to share	Numbers and the number system	Place value and ordering	9	2	130 / 131
84	Quick change	Maths to share	Calculations	Mental calculations + and –	9	3	131
85	Add and subtract 9	Practice exercise	Calculations	Mental calculations + and –	9	4	131 / 132
86	£5.00 problem	Investigation	Solving problems	Number problems in money	9	5	132
87	Quick multiplication games	Maths to share	Calculations	Mental calculations × and ÷	10	1 / 2	134
88	Double a double	Practice exercise	Calculations	Mental calculations × and ÷	10	3	135
89	Shop for sweets	Games and puzzles	Solving problems	Number problems in money	10	4	136
90	Quick double and half games	Maths to share	Numbers and the number system	Fractions	10	5	137
91	Measure up	Maths to share	Solving problems	Number problems in measures	11 / 12	1 / 3	141 / 142
92	Domino divides	Practice exercise	Calculations	Understanding × and ÷	11 / 12	1 / 3	141 / 142
93	Food trail	Maths to share	Solving problems	Number problems in measures	11 / 12	1 / 3	141 / 142
94	Sweet sort	Investigation	Solving problems	Organising and using data	11 / 12	4 / 5	143 / 144
95	Telling the time	Practice exercise	Measures, shape and space	Measures	11 / 12	6 / 9	144 / 145
96	Two-way counts	Practice exercise	Numbers and the number system	Counting and number properties	1	1 / 2	155 / 156
97	Counting on game	Maths to share	Numbers and the number system	Counting and number properties	1	3	157
98	Adding three numbers	Maths to share	Calculations	Mental calculations + and –	2 / 4	2	161
99	Find the difference	Practice exercise	Calculations	Recall of + and – facts	2 / 4	4	162
100	Four in a row	Games and puzzles	Numbers and the number system	Place value and ordering	2 / 4	5	163
101	Add/subtract 19 and 21 games	Maths to share	Calculations	Mental calculations + and –	2 / 4	6 / 7	164 / 165
102	Difference patterns	Investigation	Calculations	Mental calculations + and –	2 / 4	1 6 / 7 9	161 / 166
103	Trios	Investigation	Calculations	Mental calculations + and –	2 / 4	11	167 / 168

	100 MATHS HOMEWORK ACTIVITIES YEAR 2		NATIONAL NUMERACY STRATEGY		100 MATHS LESSONS		
PAGE IN THIS BOOK	ACTIVITY NAME	HOMEWORK	STRAND	TOPIC	NNS UNIT	LESSON	PAGE
104	Subtracting 'teens' numbers	Investigation	Calculations	Understanding + and –	2 / 4	12 / 13	168 / 169
105	Shopping with £5.00	Practice exercise	Solving problems	Number problems in money	2 / 4	15	170
106	Treasure hunt	Games and puzzles	Solving problems	Reasoning about shapes	5 / 6	1 / 5	175 / 177
107	Knock down nine-pins	Maths to share	Solving problems	Reasoning about shapes	5 / 6	1 / 5	175 / 177
108	Making carrot and orange soup	Maths to share	Solving problems	Number problems in measures	5 / 6	6	178
109	Symmetrical shapes and patterns	Investigation	Measures, shape and space	Shape and space	5 / 6	7 / 8	178 / 179
110	Count back, count on	Practice exercise	Numbers and the number system	Counting and number properties	8	1 / 3	189 / 190
111	Double it, halve it	Maths to share	Calculations	Recall of x and ÷ facts	8	4	190 / 191
112	Counting back game	Maths to share	Numbers and the number system	Counting and number properties	8	5	191
113	Hundreds and thousands	Maths to share	Calculations	Mental calculations + and –	9	1	193 / 194
114	Domino subtraction	Practice exercise	Calculations	Understanding + and –	9	2	194 / 195
115	Pay and change from £5.00	Practice exercise	Calculations	Mental calculations + and –	9	4	196
116	Subtraction game	Maths to share	Calculations	Mental calculations + and –	9	3 / 5	195 / 196
117	5 times table	Maths to share	Calculations	Mental calculations x and ÷	10 / 11	1	199 / 200
118	Double and halve	Practice exercise	Calculations	Mental calculations x and ÷	10 / 11	2 / 3	200 / 201
119	Domino multiplication	Practice exercise	Calculations	Mental calculations x and ÷	10 / 11	4	201 / 202
120	Super saver	Investigation	Solving problems	Number problems in money	10 / 11	5	202
121	Multiply and divide by 2 game	Maths to share	Calculations	Mental calculations x and ÷	10 / 11	6	203
122	Four in a line	Games and puzzles	Calculations	Mental calculations x and ÷	10 / 11	7	204
123	Shop for fruit	Maths to share	Solving problems	Number problems in money	10	8	205
124	Planning a picnic	Maths to share	Numbers and the number system	Fractions	10 / 11	9	205 / 206
125	Quartering a square puzzle	Puzzles and games	Numbers and the number system	Fractions	10 / 11	10	206
126	How much time?	Investigation	Solving problems	Number problems in measures	12 / 13	1 / 6	210 / 213 / 214
127	Travelling to London by train	Investigation	Solving problems	Number problems in measures	12 / 13	2 4 / 7 9	211 / 217
128	Mail sort	Investigation	Solving problems	Organising and using data	12 / 13	3 / 5	211 / 213

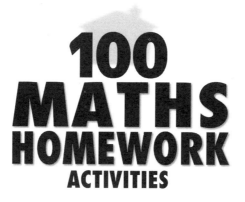

100 MATHS HOMEWORK ACTIVITIES

100 Maths Homework Activities is a series of teachers' resource books for Years 1–6. Each book is year-specific and provides a core of homework activities for mathematics within the guidelines for the National Numeracy Strategy in England. The content of these activities is also appropriate for and adaptable to the requirements of Primary 1–7 in Scottish schools.

Each book offers three terms of homework activities, matched to the termly planning in the National Numeracy Strategy *Framework for Teaching Mathematics* for that year. Schools in England and Wales that decide not to adopt the National Numeracy Strategy will still find the objectives, approaches and lesson contexts familiar and valuable. However, the teacher will need to choose from the activities to match their own requirements and planning.

The homework activities provided in the books are intended as a support for the teacher, school mathematics leader or trainee teacher. The series can be used alongside its companion series, *100 Maths Lessons and more*, or with any mathematics scheme of work, as the basis for planning homework activities throughout the school, in line with the school's homework policy. The resources can be used by teachers with single-age classes, mixed-age, single- and mixed-ability groups and for team planning of homework across a year or key stage. The teacher may also find the activities valuable for extension work in class or as additional resources for assessment.

Using the books

The activities in this book for Year 2/Primary 2–3 classes have been planned to offer a range of mathematics activities for a child to carry out at home. Many of these are designed for sharing with a helper, who can be a parent, another adult member of the family, an older sibling or a neighbour. The activities include a variety of mental arithmetic games, puzzles and practical problem-solving investigations. There are also practice exercises, some 'against the clock', to keep arithmetic skills sharp. The activities have been chosen to ensure that each strand and topic of the National Numeracy Strategy *Framework for Teaching Mathematics* is included and that the children have opportunities to develop their mental strategies, use paper-and-pencil methods appropriately, and use and apply their mathematics to solve problems.

Each of the 100 homework activities in this book includes a photocopiable page to send home. The page provides instructions for the child and a brief explanation for a helper, stating simply and clearly its purpose and suggesting support and/or a further challenge to offer the child. The mathematics strand and topic addressed by each activity and the type of homework being offered are indicated on each page. The types are shown by the following symbols:

maths to share	games and puzzles	practice exercise	investigation	timed practice exercise

There is a supporting teacher's note for each activity. These notes include:

- **Learning outcomes:** the specific learning objectives of the homework (taken from the National Numeracy Strategy *Framework for Teaching Mathematics*);
- **Lesson context:** a brief description of the classroom experience recommended for the children prior to undertaking the homework activity;
- **Setting the homework:** advice on how to explain the work to the children and set it in context before it is taken home;
- **Back at school:** suggestions for how to respond to the returned homework, such as discussion with the children or specific advice on marking, as well as answers, where relevant.

Supporting your helpers

Extensive research by the IMPACT Project (based at University of North London) has demonstrated how important parental involvement is to children's success in mathematics. A photocopiable homework diary sheet is provided on page 8 which can be sent home with the homework. This sheet has room for records of four pieces of homework and can be kept singly in a file or multiple copies stapled together to make a longer-term homework record. For each activity, there is space to record its name and the date when it was sent home and spaces for responses to the work from the helper, the child and the teacher. The homework diary is intended to encourage home–school links, so that parents and carers know what is being taught and can make informed comments about their child's progress.

Name _____

Name of activity & date sent home	Helper's comments	Child's comments		Teacher's comments
		Did you like this? Draw a face. ☺ a lot ☺ a little ☹ not much	**How much did you learn?** Draw a face. ☺ a lot ☺ a little ☹ not much	
TARGET 50p	WILLIAM ENJOYED THE GAME – HE PLAYED IT WITH ME AND HIS DAD.	☺	☺	Great to hear that William enjoyed playing the game with you and his Dad. Try target £1.00 using the same rules.
ADDING TWO TEENS NUMBERS	WILLIAM KEPT GETTING THE ANSWERS WRONG AND NEEDED A LOT OF HELP.	☺	☺	I'll give William more help with adding tens and units. As he enjoyed the money game, let him try adding two sums of money between 10p and 15p, using 10p and 1p coins for the tens and units.

Using the activities with *100 Maths Lessons* series

The organisation of the homework activities in this book matches the planning grids within *100 Maths Lessons and more: Year 2* (also written by Suzanne Edwards and published by Scholastic), so that there is homework matching the learning objectives covered in each unit of work in each term. Grids, including details of which lessons in *100 Maths Lessons and more: Year 2* have associated homework activities in *100 Maths Homework Activities*, with the relevant page numbers, are provided on pages 2–5 in this book to help teachers using *100 Maths Lessons and more: Year 2* with their planning.

About this book: Year 2/Primary 2–3

This book contains four types of homework activities, all recommended by the NNS for children in Year 2/ Primary 2–3: 'Maths to share', 'Investigations', 'Games and puzzles' and 'Practice exercises'. All the 'Maths to share' activities encourage the child and a helper to work together to carry out the tasks within home contexts. The 'Investigations' and 'Games and Puzzles' involve a mix of mental arithmetic and strategy games for two or more players. The 'Practice exercises' provide children with opportunities for further practice of number and 'four rules' work done in school and to keep mental arithmetic skills sharp. These activities are designed for children to work on independently at their own pace, or 'against the clock' as an extension activity. For these activities, helpers are given guidance on ways to help if their child gets stuck.

Use of equipment and the resource pages

The majority of the homework activities require no resources or specify the use of household equipment or resources that are commonly available at home or can be purchased cheaply such as packs of playing cards, dice or dominoes. Pages 27 and 28 provide resources required regularly to support the homework sheets.

Reading the instructions on the homework sheets

In Year 2/Primary 2–3 classes, children are at different stages of learning to read. To help the child read the instructions on the homework sheets, it is suggested that some guidance is given to helpers on using progressive 'shared reading' at home according to a child's reading ability. Illustrations to support reading together are provided on many of the pages.

Year 2 SATs

The activities in this homework book are not designed to coach or otherwise prepare children for SATs specifically, however, their growing confidence and facility with numbers will inevitably support the children's performance in the tests.

Name _____

Name of activity & date sent home	Helper's comments	Child's comments	Teacher's comments
		Did you like this? Draw a face. ☺ a lot · :| a little · ☹ not much	**How much did you learn?** Draw a face. ☺ a lot · :| a little · ☹ not much	

Teachers' notes

TERM 1

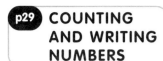 **COUNTING AND WRITING NUMBERS**   PRACTICE EXERCISE

Learning outcome
- **Read and write whole numbers** in figures.

Lesson context
Count orally in ones from 0–100 as a class. Give each group a shuffled set of 1–50 numeral cards. In each group, one child deals out all the cards. The child with the 1-card lays it down on the table, then the child with the 2-card lays it beside the 1 and so on. Challenge the children to write the numbers 1–50 (or as far as they can) in order on squared paper.

Setting the homework
Show the children the activity sheet and read out the instructions.

Back at school
Annotate each child's work with appropriate comments. Make a note of the last number written if the child did not reach 49. Children who have difficulty writing numbers up to 20 may need further experience using a printed number line until they are confident with their 'mental number line'. Note whether any child commonly writes any digit or number in reverse.

 **COUNTING OBJECTS ON A TRAY**   MATHS TO SHARE

Learning outcome
- Count reliably up to 100 objects by grouping them in tens.

Lesson context
Ask the children to count sets of objects in tubs within the range of 10–50 and record results. Encourage the children to arrange objects into piles of tens and find the total by counting on in tens and adding on any remaining 'ones'.

Setting the homework
Explain the activity to the children.

Back at school
Comment on each child's work. Note if the child has counted objects in the range 10–50, 10–20 or 50–100.

 **COUNTING ON IN ONES**   MATHS TO SHARE

Learning outcome
- **Count on in ones, starting from any two-digit number.**

Lesson context
Ask the class to count on ten in ones from numbers you point to on a 0–99 chart. Give each child a 0–99 grid, a small cube and paper for recording. Children throw the cube on to the grid to establish a number, write it down, then continue to write numbers counting on in ones to the number that is ten more. Repeat the activity counting back.

Setting the homework
Show the children the activity sheet. Read out the instructions and check that the children understand what they have to do. For children working with numbers up to 20, tell them to ask their Helper to write numbers between 1 and 10 in the first boxes on the sheet before they carry out the activity.

Back at school
Check and comment on the children's work. Note whether the child has written numbers within the range 1–50, 1–20 or 1–100. Children with difficulty working with numbers to 20 may need further experience of counting on and writing numbers with the help of a printed number line.

p32 **COUNTING ON AND BACK IN ONES**   PRACTICE EXERCISE

Learning outcome
- **Count on and back in ones, starting from any two-digit number.**

Lesson context
Count on and/or back one from numbers on the 0–99 chart as a class. Ask the children to repeat the activity by throwing a cube on to a 0–99 grid to establish a number, then count on/back one from that number: 66 ← 67 → 68. (Record using photocopiable page 28 of *100 Maths Lessons: Year 2*, if available). Less able children can choose start numbers from a set of 1–20 cards. More able children can try 'count on/count back 2'.

Setting the homework
Explain they will be repeating the activity at home. For children working with numbers up to 20, tell them to ask their Helper to write numbers between 1 and 19 in the middle boxes.

Back at school
Note whether child has counted within the range 1–99, 1–19 or used the rule 'count on/count back 2' or 'count on/count back 10'. Children who had difficulties may need the help of a printed number line.

p33 **10 GAME**   MATHS TO SHARE

Learning outcome
- **Know by heart: all pairs of numbers with a total of 10.** (Year 1 revision)

Lesson context
Give each child some paper and a pile of playing cards, Ace–10 (Ace = 1). Each child turns over a card from the pile and writes a sum using the number on the card and the number needed to make 10; for example, 6 + 4 = 10.

Setting the homework
Show the children the sheet, read out the instructions and check the children's understanding.

Back at school
Play a version of the game where you say a number between 1 and 10 and choose a child to say the number needed to make 10.

p34 **ADDING TWO NUMBERS**   INVESTIGATION

Learning outcomes
- **Know by heart: all addition and subtraction facts for each number to at least 10.**
- Use the + and = sign to record mental calculations in a number sentence.

Lesson context
Give two sets of 1–10 numeral cards to each child or group. Ask the children to write down as many addition sums as they can using one number from each set. Highlight using 'doubles' and demonstrate 'putting the larger number first' and adding the second number by counting on mentally.

Setting the homework
Show the children the homework, read out the instructions and check understanding. Any child who worked with numbers 1 to 5 in school should do the same at home.

Back at school
Any child who had difficulty may need experience of adding with the help of a printed number line.

p35 TENS AND UNITS
PRACTICE EXERCISE

Learning outcome
- **Know what each digit in a two-digit number represents, including 0 as a place holder,** and partition two-digit numbers into a multiple of tens and ones (TU).

Lesson context
Use a prepared sheet showing drawings of tens and units spike abaci with a number within the range 10–99 written underneath each. Tell the children to draw beads on each abacus to show the given number. For children just starting work with tens and units, write numbers between 10 and 30 underneath each abacus and tell them to make each number with Cuisenaire rods before they draw the beads.

Setting the homework
Explain they will need to throw a cube onto a 0–99 grid and write the number it lands on on the sheet before they draw in the beads. Tell any child working with numbers up to 30 in school to ask their Helper to write numbers 10–30 for them instead.

Back at school
Any child who had difficulty may need guidance with partitioning two-digit numbers into tens and units using Cuisenaire rods.

p36 DOUBLING NUMBERS
PRACTICE EXERCISE

Learning outcomes
- Derive quickly: doubles of all numbers to at least 15.
- Partition additions into tens and units, then recombine.

Lesson context
Explain doubling a 'teens' number by grouping the tens, then the units, and then recombining them to find the total. Let the children practise doubling by drawing cards from a 10–20 pack and recording as doubling sums: 14+14. Use 1–10 cards for children who are unsure of doubling 'teens numbers'.

Setting the homework
Check that they understand what to do. Children who have difficulty with doubling numbers above 10, should work with numbers 1–9 only.

Back at school
To help any child who had difficulty, plan an activity using two sets of Ace–10 playing cards. Children select two cards showing the same number, say the number on the first card, then double it by counting on the spots on the second card. For more able children, change to two sets of 1–10 numeral cards.

p37 TARGET 50p
MATHS TO SHARE

Learning outcome
- Use mental addition and subtraction to solve simple problems involving money.

Lesson context
Set up a shopping activity to buy two items ranging in cost from 5p to 25p and work out change from 50p. Show the children how to find the total by writing the larger amount first then adding on the smaller amount. Now find the change by counting on from the total to 50p.

Setting the homework
Explain the rules. Give the children an opportunity to play the game with a partner before they take it home.

Back at school
Plan for children to play the game with a partner or in a small group when they have finished other work.

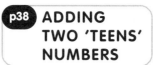

p38 ADDING TWO 'TEENS' NUMBERS
PRACTICE EXERCISE

Learning outcome
- **Use knowledge that addition can be done in any order to do mental calculations more efficiently.** For example: put the larger number first and count on in tens and ones.

Lesson context
Demonstrate how to add two 'teens' numbers by partitioning; for example, $15 + 11 \rightarrow 10 + 10 + 5 + 1 \rightarrow 20 + 5 = 25$. Place a set of numeral cards 10–20 in two rows on each table. Ask the children to select a number from each row to add together using partitioning and record their sums.

Setting the homework
Enlarge a diagram from the sheet and demonstrate the activity.

Back at school
Check work for errors. Any child who had difficulty may need further guidance with partitioning two-digit numbers.

p39 20 GAME
MATHS TO SHARE

Learning outcome
- **Know by heart:** all pairs of numbers with a total of 20.

Lesson context
Use a pile of 1–20 numeral cards for each child. Ask them to turn over a card and write a sum using the number on the card and the number needed to make 20 each time.

Setting the homework
Show the children the sheet and check that they understand it.

Back at school
Play a version of the homework game: say a number between 1 and 20 and choose a child to say the number needed to make 20.

p40 ADD AND SUBTRACT 10
PRACTICE EXERCISE

Learning outcome
- Say the number that is 10 more or less than any given two-digit number.

Lesson context
Point to numbers on a 0–99 chart and ask individual children to count on and/or back ten from each. Children throw a cube onto a 0–99 grid to establish a number and record counting on and back 10.

Setting the homework
Show the children the sheet and check that they understand it.

Back at school
Challenge them to try 'count on/count back 30'. Children who had difficulty may need experience of counting on 10 with the help of a 0–49 number rectangle until they start to recognise a patten.

 £1.00 PROBLEM

INVESTIGATION

Learning outcomes
• Recognise all coins and begin to use £ notation.
• Find totals and work out which coins to pay.

Lesson context
Demonstrate using £ notation to record amounts £1.00 and above. You will need three dice or cubes with their six faces marked: 2p, 5p, 10p, 20p, 50p, £1.00, a set of all coins, a tray and paper for each group. Children work in pairs. They take turns to throw the dice in the tray and write the score as a money sum. They should write the amounts from each dice in the easiest order to find the total. For children who may find this difficult, use only two dice/cubes.

Setting the homework
Demonstrate the task. Tell children who are only confident working with money amounts to 50p to find ways to make 50p instead of £1.00.

Back at school
Check work for errors. Repeat the activity in class, asking the children to start with ten 10p coins, then exchange the coins for others of equivalent value.

 ESTIMATING AND MEASURING LENGTH

MATHS TO SHARE

Learning outcome
• **Estimate, measure and compare lengths using standard units** (m, cm).

Lesson context
For each group provide rulers, paper and a set of small objects that can be measured in centimetres. Draw the following chart on a flip chart/chalkboard for the children to copy or prepare worksheets:

Name of object	Estimate (cm)	Actual length (cm)

Tell the children to write the name of an object on the chart, followed by their estimate of its length. Finally, they can measure the object with a ruler and write down the actual length.

Setting the homework
When finished, the children should order the objects measured by size, starting with the shortest.

Back at school
Review the results of the homework activity using a large copy of the chart. Choose different children to name an object and its length, for you to write on to the chart. Ask the class to order the objects in size, longest to shortest.

 MEASURE UP

MATHS TO SHARE

Learning outcome
• **Measure and compare lengths using standard units** (m, cm).

Lesson context
Provide each child with a chart with ten body parts for them to measure listed in the first column. Include parts to measure around such as the head, wrist or ankle. Tell the children to work with a partner to measure parts of each other's bodies in centimetres and then work out the difference in centimetres between their measurements and their partner's.

Setting the homework
Show the children the activity and check that they understand it.

Back at school
Review the results of the homework. Draw the chart using the headings 'Helper 1' and 'Helper 2'. Ask two children to say the length of their Helper's hand and write the results on the chart. Ask the class to work out the difference between the two.

 HUNT FOR CIRCLES AND SPHERES

INVESTIGATION

Learning outcomes
• **Use the mathematical names for common 3-D and 2-D shapes.**
• **Sort shapes and describe some of their features.**

Lesson context
Make a copy of the following chart for each child:

Properties of shapes		
Name of shape	Flat shape Number of sides	Solid shape Number of faces

Use a mixed set of 2–D and 3–D shapes for each group. Tell the children to write the name of a shape on the chart, then count the number of sides or faces.

Setting the homework
Show the children the sheet and check they understand it.

Back at school
Copy the chart from the homework sheet. Ask each child to name an object found at home and say whether it was a circle or a sphere. Record this information. Go through the list and get a show of hands. Count the hands and write the number next to the name of the object. Consider most/fewest etc.

 SHAPES MADE FROM FIVE SQUARES

GAMES AND PUZZLES

Learning outcome
• Solve mathematical puzzles. Suggest extensions by asking 'What if…? or 'What could I try next?'

Lesson context
Ask the children to make different shapes on 9-pin geoboards with elastic bands and draw them on dotty paper. Colour the shapes and write the name of any shape they recognise underneath it.

Setting the homework
Tell the children to ask their Helper to cut out five newspaper squares. Demonstrate using five squares Blu-Tacked onto a flip chart. Emphasise that the sides of two squares must touch.

Back at school
Check through each child's work. Draw rings around any shapes that are identical, but facing a different way, and join them with a line. There are 12 possible solutions.

 MY NUMBER/ YOUR NUMBER GAMES

MATHS TO SHARE

Learning outcome
• **Describe and extend simple number sequences.**

Lesson context
Demonstrate how to colour the pattern of 'counting in twos' from zero on a 0–99 grid and how to record the pattern as a number sequence underneath: $0 \rightarrow 2 \rightarrow 4…$ and so on. Encourage prediction. Give each child a 0–99 grid to copy and continue colouring and writing the pattern.

Setting the homework
Explain to the children that they are to play each game on the sheet with their Helper. Use the first game as an example.

Back at school
Repeat the games as circle games, where the first child says 'one', the second child says 'two' and so on.

p47 ODD AND EVEN DOMINOES

INVESTIGATION

Learning outcomes
- **Recognise odd and even numbers** to at least 30.
- Investigate a general statement about familiar numbers by finding examples that satisfy it.

Lesson context
Demonstrate the rules determining odd and even numbers. Give each group a set of dominoes and prepare the following chart for them:

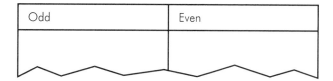

Odd	Even

Each group spreads their dominoes out face down on the table. Each child selects a domino, counts the total number of spots and decides whether the number is odd or even. They then draw a picture of the domino in the correct column and write the number beside it. If the children are unsure of odd and even numbers, provide them with 12 interlocking cubes to make each domino number in a stick of cubes. Split the stick into twos and see whether there are any odd ones left.

Setting the homework
Show the children the sheet and check that they understand it.

Back at school
Check work for errors. Play a circle game where you give each child a 1–30 numeral card. They say whether their number is odd or even.

p48 SCORING 12 WITH THREE CARDS

GAMES AND PUZZLES

Learning outcome
- Solve mathematical problems. Suggest extensions by asking ' What if...? or 'What could I try next?'

Lesson context
Using sets of three spotted 1–6 dice, ask the children to work with a partner to find ways to score 12 with three dice. Ask the children to record their solutions individually as dice drawings and by writing an addition beside each.

Setting the homework
Show the children the sheet and check that they understand it.

Back at school
Review the homework. Invite children to say their different solutions for you. Ask the children to mark their own work by drawing a tick beside the same solution on their sheet, even if it has the same numbers, but in a different order.

p49 ROUNDING NUMBERS

PRACTICE EXERCISE

Learning outcome
- Round numbers less than 100 to the nearest 10.

Lesson context
Explain and demonstrate the principle of rounding numbers to the nearest ten. Point to different numbers on a 0–99 chart and ask individuals to round each number to the nearest ten. Children throw a cube onto a 0–99 grid and write down the number it lands on. They note down the number rounded to the nearest ten, for example 78 → 80.

Setting the homework
Explain that they will be practising rounding numbers to the nearest ten by repeating the number square and cube game.

Back at school
Check each child's work for errors. Repeat, asking individuals to round numbers you point to on a 0–99 chart, to the nearest ten.

p50 ORDERING NUMBERS

MATHS TO SHARE

Learning outcome
- Use and begin to read the vocabulary of comparing and ordering numbers, including ordinal numbers, to 30.

Lesson context
Play circle games with sets of ordinal number cards 1st–30th (or more). Give out the ordinal cards in numerical order and say: *Will the child holding the fourth card stand up?* Repeat, starting with a different number. Ask the children to say the numbers in order round the circle 1st to 30th. Give each group a set of ordinal cards. One child in each group deals out the set. Children take turns to lay the cards in a line in order. If the second child does not have the '2nd' card, play passes to the third child. First child to put down all their cards is the winner.

Setting the homework
Show the children the sheet and check they understand it.

Back at school
Check through each child's work identifying any errors. Make a note of any child who only worked with numbers to 20.

p51 ADDING THREE NUMBERS

GAMES AND PUZZLES

Learning outcome
- **Use knowledge that addition can be done in any order to do mental calculations more efficiently.** For example: add three small numbers by putting the largest number first and/or finding a pair totalling 10.

Lesson context
Demonstrate adding three numbers less than 20, starting with the largest number. Lay a shuffled set of numeral cards 1–20 in two lines of ten cards on each table and provide some small triangle templates. Demonstrate how the children should draw around a triangle, then select three number cards including one 'teens' number. They write a number beside each corner of the triangle and find the total by starting from the largest number, then counting on the other numbers in the easiest order. They write the total in the centre of the triangle. Tell them to repeat this ten times.

Setting the homework
Remind the children to start from the largest number, then to add or count on the other numbers in the easiest order.

Back at school
Check the children's work for errors. Congratulate any child who worked with four dice.

p52 PAY AND CHANGE FROM 50p

PRACTICE EXERCISE

Learning outcome
- Find totals, give change, and work out which coins to pay.

Lesson context
Use sets of three money dice marked 1p, 2p, 5p, 10p, 10p, 20p and a copy of the following chart for each child:

Money spent in coins	Total	Change in coins	Total change

Working with a partner, tell the children to take turns to roll the money dice to establish which coins are spent. They should draw around coins on the sheet, find the total and then write it in. They should work out the change from 50p, writing the total and drawing possible coins in the change column. They should record their answer in the same way. Use two dice for less able children.

Setting the homework
Highlight that they must select the three amounts of money 'to pay' from the boxes on the sheet.

Back at school
Check the children's work for errors.

p53 FOOT WORK

Learning outcome
- **Understand the operation of multiplication as repeated addition.**

Lesson context
Introduce 'times 2'. Use 12 numbered plastic bank bags containing different numbers of 2p coins ranging from 10p–50p in value. Divide the bags between the tables. Make a copy of the following chart for each child:

Bag number	Number of 2p coins	Total amount of money

Children work with a partner to count the number of coins, then count the total amount by counting in twos. Replace the money in the bag and take another. When they have counted all the bags on their table, they can move to count the bags on other tables.

Setting the homework
Show the children the sheet and check that they understand it.

Back at school
Invite different children to say the number of coins that covered their foot and how much their footprint was worth. Scribe the results. Ask the class: *Which child's foot is worth the least/most amount of money?*

p54 DOMINO MULTIPLICATION

Learning outcomes
- **Know by heart: multiplication facts for the 2 times table.**
- Use the × and = sign to record mental calculations in a number sentence.

Lesson context
Give each group a tray of interlocking cubes at their table. Demonstrate how to build up the 2 times table by grouping cubes into sets of two. Ask the children to make a stick of two cubes. Write $2 \times 1 = 2$ on the flip chart. Ask them to make another stick of two cubes. Write $2 \times 2 = 4$ on the chart. The children make another stick of two cubes, then ask: *What should be written next?* They then copy the 'times 2 number sentences' to their sheet and then continue making sticks of two cubes and writing the 2 times table.

Setting the homework
Demonstrate the method of recording shown on the sheet.

Back at school
Check the work for errors and signal that it has been seen and approved. Congratulate children who multiplied by 10.

p55 HAND WORK

Learning outcome
- **Understand the operation of multiplication as repeated addition.**

Lesson context
Sit the children in a circle, count around in tens from 0–100 and 100–0, then give each child a card marked '10'. Ask a number of children to stand up and show their cards, for example five children. Ask: *How many tens? How many altogether?* Prepare ten numbered plastic bank bags containing different numbers of 10p coins from one to ten. Divide the bags up between the groups to carry out the activity in the same way as page 53 'Foot work'.

Setting the homework
Demonstrate the activity by holding up your fingers and choosing a child to say the total and the number needed to make 100.

Back at school
Repeat the homework activity in a spare moment in class.

p56 £1.00 TO SPEND AT THE PAPER SHOP

Learning outcome
- Find totals, give change, and work out which coins to pay.

Lesson context
Set up a shopping activity where the children find ways to buy two items from six, ranging from 5p to 75p, and work out the change from £1.00. Alternatively, design an activity using a different theme, e.g., at the 'Zoo shop' or 'Toy shop'. Encourage the children to find the total by starting from the larger amount and then adding the smaller amount by counting on.

Setting the homework
Read the title and the names and cost of each item. Explain to the children that they will be practising finding the cost of two items and change from £1.00.

Back at school
Check through the children's work for errors and congratulate any child who bought three items each time.

p57 WAYS TO HALVE A PIZZA

Learning outcome
- Begin to recognise and find one half of shapes and small numbers of objects.

Lesson context
Children find out how many different ways there are to place half of six eggs in a six-egg (half-dozen) box. Show the children an egg box. Ask: *How many eggs will fit in the box? How many is half?* Draw a 3 × 2 grid and show the positions of three eggs:

Give the children squared paper, coloured pencils, Plasticine and an egg box. Tell them to make three Plasticine 'eggs', and find ways to place them in box, recording results on squared paper by drawing 3 × 2 grids as egg boxes and a circle for each egg.

Setting the home work
Remind the children of the egg-box activity. Explain the homework is to find ways to halve an eight-slice pizza.

Back at school
Draw some 'pizza' diagrams and invite the children to colour in a solution. Ask the children to mark their work by drawing a tick beside any solution that is the same as one on the chart.

p58 BAKING CAKES

Learning outcomes
- **Measure masses using standard units.**
- **Read a simple scale to the nearest labelled division.**

Lesson context
Demonstrate how a wide selection of weighing equipment works. Write a list of the equipment on the board. Children suggest items that each piece of equipment might weigh. Give each child a sheet of A4 paper folded in half. They write the name of a piece of weighing equipment in the top half, then draw and label four things that could be weighed with it in the bottom half.

Setting the homework
Tell the children to bake some cakes at home with their Helper. Read out the list of ingredients and the method. They should ask their Helper to let them weigh all the ingredients and prepare the mixture. Emphasise they must not attempt this by themselves.

Back at school
Ask the children to say what type of weighing equipment they used and to describe how they made their cakes.

p59 BALL GAMES

Learning outcome
• Order days of the week and months of the year.

Lesson context
Use a set of flash cards of the months of the year for each group. One child deals out all the cards. The child with 'January' lays their card at the end of the table, and play passes to the child with 'February', who lays it under the 'January' card and so on. Repeat the game and then challenge the children to write the names of the months in order.

Setting the homework
Use a ball to play the 'Names of days of the week' game.

Back at school
Ask, with a show of hands: *Who was able to throw and catch a ball saying all the names of the days of the week without dropping the ball? ...say all the names of the months of the year? Did anyone try bouncing the ball? ...throwing the ball?*

p60 TV TIMES

Learning outcomes
• Solve a given problem by sorting, classifying and ordering information in a table.
• Use and begin to read the vocabulary related to time.

Lesson context
Use sets of 12 time cards showing each hour from 1–12 o'clock. Prepare a worksheet titled 'Later and earlier' with lines of three clocks side by side. Use a clock stamp. Make a copy of the sheet for each child. (Use photocopiable page 90 from *100 Maths Lesson: Year 2*, if available.) Spread a set of time cards out face down on each table. The children pick up a card and draw hands on the first middle clock to show that time and write the time underneath. Then they work out 'one hour earlier' and 'one hour later' and draw in the hands on the clocks either side and write the times underneath.

Setting the homework
Tell the children to ask their Helper to help them find today's TV programmes in a newspaper, magazine or on Teletext. Demonstrate an example of the recording. Tell them to leave any row blank if there is not a programme that starts at that time.

Back at school
Draw the following chart on the class board:

Time	BBC 1	BBC 2	ITV	Channel 4	Channel 5
3 o'clock					
4 o'clock...					

Ask a child to name the channel, the name of their favourite programme and the starting time. Scribe the results in the correct positions. Ask, with a show of hands, how many children chose that programme as their favourite. Write the number beside the programme. When all the results are on the chart ask: *Which programme was chosen by the most/fewest/same number of children?*

p61 TIMING GAMES

Learning outcome
• Use and begin to read the vocabulary related to time.

Lesson context
Tell the children to see how many numbers they can write in 1 minute, counting from 1, while you time them. Ask them to write down their estimate first. Repeat the game to see if they can beat their score. Tell them to use the back of their paper to see how many times they can write their name (first and family name) in 1 minute, estimating first.

Setting the homework
The first timing game to play is the task they did in school. Can they beat their score?

Back at school
Ask the children to look at the results of others to find out the highest number written. Ask each group to give their results. Ask questions as before.

p62 HUNT FOR CUPBOARDS AND DRAWERS

Learning outcome
• Solve a given problem by sorting, classifying and organising information in a table.

Lesson context
Make a large wall pictogram with 12 columns for the names of the months. Each child draws a picture of their face, cuts it out and pastes it in the appropriate column for their birthday. Display the completed chart and ask: *Which month shows the most/fewest birthdays? Do any months show the same number of birthdays? What is the total number of birthdays in... and... ? If two more children had birthdays in..., how many would there be together?*

Setting the homework
Tell the children they are detectives hunting for and counting all the cupboards and drawers in each room to complete the charts.

Back at school
Copy the second chart on to the board. Ask a child to give the greatest number of cupboards they found in one room. Ask, with a show of hands: *Did anyone find more cupboards than that in one room?* Write the highest number of cupboards found in one room on the chart. Repeat with fewest cupboards.

TERM 2

p63 COUNTING AND WRITING NUMBERS 99–0
PRACTICE EXERCISE

Learning outcome
- **Describe and extend simple number sequences: count back in ones.**

Lesson context
In your mental maths time, count back in ones from 100. Demonstrate with a 0–99 chart how to throw a cube on to a square to establish a start number. The children record this number and then count back in ones to the number that is five less, for example 63 → 62 → 61 → 60 → 59 → 58. Encourage the children to use their fingers to keep track of the count.

Setting the homework
Show the children the activity sheet and read out the instructions.

Back at school
Look through each child's work and comment. Note whether any child writes any digit or number in reverse. Highlight correct forms. Congratulate any child who completed a 100 to 199 number square.

p64 ODD AND EVEN TELEPHONE NUMBERS
INVESTIGATION

Learning outcome
- **Recognise odd and even numbers** to at least 30.

Lesson context
Give each group a set of dominoes to spread out face down on a table. Each child selects two dominoes, counts the spots on each and writes the two numbers as a sum with the total and decides whether the total number is an odd or even number.

Setting the homework
Copy the chart on to the board. Invite children to say their telephone numbers. Show how to add the digits together, starting with the highest number or a pair to make 10. Count on the remaining numbers to find the total. Write a tick to show whether the number is odd or even.

Back at school
Copy the chart from the sheet and complete it with examples from the children's sheets.

p65 COUNTING IN HUNDREDS
MATHS TO SHARE

Learning outcome
- **Describe and extend simple number sequences:** count in hundreds from and back to zero.

Lesson context
Write a 'hundreds' number on the board. Ask the children to say the number followed by the 'count on 100' number; for example, 300 → 400. Repeat with 'count back 100', for example 300 → 200. Give the children a set of hundreds cards 100–900. They choose a card and write down the number followed by the 'count on 100' number, then repeat with the rule 'count back 100'.

Setting the homework
Tell the children to play the game with members of their family, if they wish.

Back at school
Plan for the children to play the game with a partner or in a small group.

p66 NUMBER SQUARES
PRACTICE EXERCISE

Learning outcome
- **Order whole numbers to at least 100,** and position them on a 100 square.

Lesson context
Use a blank hundred chart to demonstrate how to find the position of any number the children call out: count down the first column in tens, then count along in ones. Deal each group ten cards and tell them to write the numbers in the correct places on their blank number squares. Have 0–99 grids available as support. Deal more able children 20 cards.

Setting the homework
Explain how the children have to write the correct, missing numbers in the shaded squares.

Back at school
Complete an enlarged copy of the homework sheet. Ask the children to draw a ring around each correct number on their homework sheet. Children who rounded numbers to the nearest 10 give their answers and mark them in the same way.

p67 TARGET 50
GAMES AND PUZZLES

Learning outcomes
- **Order whole numbers to at least 100.**
- **Know what each digit in a two-digit number represents, including 0 as a place holder.**

Lesson context
Give each group a set of 1–100 numeral cards. Each child counts out seven cards, places them in order, lowest to highest, and then records the numbers. Used cards are placed in a tub. When all cards have been used, the cards are reshuffled and reused until everyone has ordered ten sets. Provide 0–99 grids, if support is required.

Setting the homework
Draw two 'Tens and ones' score charts on the board. Give two children two cards each. Ask each child to make the nearest number they can to 50, in tens and ones (above or below 50), and write it on a score chart. Ask the class to say which score is nearer to 50.

Back at school
Plan for the children to play the homework game with a partner or in small group.

p68 CHANGE PLEASE!
MATHS TO SHARE

Learning outcome
- Use mental addition and subtraction to solve simple problems involving money.

Lesson context
Make up a set of 20 money bags (numbered 1–20) each containing a different amount of money (50p to £1.00). Divide the bags between the groups. Demonstrate how to sort the coins by type, then, starting with the total of the highest value coin, add the total of the next value coin and so on. Explain £.p notation. Ask the children to work in pairs to find the total in each bag.

Setting the homework
Demonstrate giving change by counting on. Draw pictures of the coins as each is counted.

Back at school
Set up a 'till' using tubs as described. Act out the activity with you as the customer and different children giving you change in the 'shopkeeper's way'. Choose another child to check if the change is correct.

p69 ADDING TWO-DIGIT NUMBERS

PRACTICE EXERCISE

Learning outcome
* Partition additions into tens and units, then recombine.

Lesson context
Demonstrate adding two two-digit numbers by placing the larger number first and partitioning the numbers into tens and units. The children select two cards from a 10–50 set and add the numbers together, recording their workings. Less able children make the numbers with Cuisenaire rods and regroup them to find the total.

Setting the homework
Children to work mentally where they can, but to write workings, by splitting each number into tens and units, if they are unsure.

Back at school
Ask, with a show of hands: *Who completed more than ten sums? ...20? ...30?* Hold up two cards from a 11–30 set. Choose a child to say the total.

p70 SCORING 30 WITH THREE CARDS

GAMES AND PUZZLES

Learning outcome
* Solve mathematical problems or puzzles. Suggest extensions by asking: 'What if...?' or 'What could I try next?'

Lesson context
Tell the children to find different ways to make 30 using three numbers. Demonstrate how to record each way by drawing a triangle, writing a number beside each corner then writing 30 inside. Tell them to check that the numbers add up to 30 by adding them in a different way each time. Encourage more able children to use subtraction too.

Setting the homework
Choose a child to demonstrate how the game is played.

Back at school
Look through each child's work and comment. Let the children play the game with a partner.

p71 SORTING AND COUNTING CASH

MATHS TO SHARE

Learning outcome
* Recognise all coins and begin to use £.p notation for money. Find totals.

Lesson context
As in 'Change please!' (see note for page 68), but with amounts from £1.00 to £3.00.

Setting the homework
Show the children the homework sheet and read out the instructions. Tell the children to sort the coins into type, count the amounts in each pile and write down the totals.

Back at school
Look through each child's work and review it. Copy the chart from the sheet and ask different children to read a result for you to write on to it. Start with £2.00 coins on Day 1 and finish with 1p coins on Day 3. Ask the children to find the total amount of £2.00 coins, then £1.00 coins and so on.

p72 ADDING THREE TWO-DIGIT NUMBERS

INVESTIGATION

Learning outcome
* Begin to add three two-digit numbers with the help of apparatus.

Lesson context
Demonstrate how to add three two-digit numbers by partitioning with the help of Cuisenaire rods.
For example: $23 + 14 + 12 \rightarrow 4$ tens and 9 units $\rightarrow 40 + 9 = 49$. Place a set of 10–29 numeral cards in two lines of ten cards on each table. Tell the children to select three numbers to add together and record their workings. Encourage more able children to work mentally.

Setting the homework
Show the children the sheet and read out the instructions. Tell them they will be practising adding three two-digit numbers with the same method they have been using in school. Demonstrate the method of working and recording.

Back at school
Invite three children to give you a number between 10 and 30. Write the numbers on the board and ask a child to write the sum, in order, with the largest number first. Ask the class to work out the total. Choose a child to write their method on the board. Ask the children to verify whether the answer is correct.

p73 PAY AND RECEIVE CHANGE FROM £2.00

PRACTICE EXERCISE

Learning outcome
* Find totals, give change, and work out which coins to pay.

Lesson context
Give each pair three money dice (two: 1p, 2p, 5p, 10p, 20p, 50p; and one: 50p, 50p, 50p, £1.00, £1.00, £1.00) and a copy of the following chart each.

Money spent in coins	Total	Change in coins	Total change

Pairs take turns to throw the three dice to determine the total spent. They draw round coins on the chart, find the total and then write it in. They work out the change from £2.00, writing the total change and drawing possible coins in the change column. Use two dice for less able children.

Setting the homework
Show the children the sheet and read out the instructions. Explain that this time they must select three amounts of money.

Back at school
Check work for errors. If correct, signal that the work has been seen and approved. Congratulate any child who worked with change from £3.00.

p74 A SPECIAL TREAT

Learning outcomes
- Find totals, give change, and work out which coins to pay.
- Use mental addition and subtraction to solve simple problems in 'real life' involving money.

Lesson context
Display this menu:

Hot snacks	Sweets	Drinks
Small burger 70p	Cake 25p	Small milk 20p
Large burger £1.00	Biscuits 10p	Large milk 40p
Hot dog 90p	Choc-ice 15p	Small cola 30p
Double burger £1.50	Apple 20p	Large cola 50p
Chips 40p	Banana 20p	Orange juice 45p

Ask the children to find six different combinations of: a hot snack, a sweet and a drink, for under £2.00 and find out how much change they would get. Encourage them to start from the largest amount of money and count on the smaller amounts to find the total. Tell them to find the change using the 'shopkeeper's method'.

Setting the homework
This activity can be done 'for real' if they are being taken out for a meal, e.g., during a shopping trip. If they do this, then they should not complete the sheet until they have been for their meal and then bring the sheet to school to share the event.

Back at school
Ask any child who had a meal to say where they went, what they ate, what their Helper chose and how much the meal cost. Keep each child's sheet in a class book.

p75 CONTAINER HUNT

Learning outcome
- **Compare capacities using standard units** (litre, millilitre, kilogram, gram).

Lesson context
Make a copy of the following chart on A3 paper for each group:

Bottles	Cans	Tubs
Packets	Jars	Bags

Discuss what items are packaged in each type of container. Have one of each type available. Tell the children to think of different dry and wet items and work together to list five items that are packaged in each type of container.

Setting the homework
Show the children the sheet and read out the instructions. Emphasise they must work with their Helper on this activity. Explain there may be items in cupboards that are breakable, too heavy for them or should not to be handled unsupervised.

Back at school
Make a large copy of the homework chart. For each heading, the children, in turn, name an item from their sheet and say how much the container holds. List these on the class chart. Tell the children to draw a tick against the item if they have it on their sheet.

p76 POURING DRINKS

Learning outcome
- **Estimate, measure and compare capacities using standard units** (litre).

Lesson context
Use a plastic 1 litre bottle, a set of smaller containers of different capacities, a funnel, a washing-up bowl and a copy of the following chart for each group:

Ways to fill a litre measure		
Container	Estimate	Check by pouring and counting

Copy the chart on to flip chart/chalkboard. Demonstrate estimating and filling a litre bottle with one of the small containers and recording results. Where a container does not fill the litre bottle, discuss measures such as 5½ or '5 and a bit'. Let the children work with a partner or in small groups, taking turns to estimate and fill the litre bottle.

Setting the homework
Show the children the sheet and check that they understand it.

Back at school
Draw the chart from the homework activity on to the board. Fill in the chart together from the class's results. Ask: *Which estimates are more/less than the actual number? Which container filled the least/most cups? Are there any containers that filled the same number of cups?*

p77 HUNT FOR SQUARES AND CUBES

Learning outcomes
- **Use the mathematical names for common 3–D and 2–D shapes.**
- **Sort shapes and describe some of their features.**

Lesson context
Ask the children to make at least three different solid shapes from Polydron or Clixi and write a sentence about each shape, e.g.: 'My first shape has four triangle faces and one square face.'

Setting the homework
Hold up a square and a cube. Make sure the children understand what they have to do.

Back at school
Copy the chart from the homework sheet on to the flip chart/board. Ask each child to name an object from home and say whether it was square or a cube. Fill in the class chart. Ask, with a show of hands: *Who found a... at home?* Write the number next to the object each time. Ask: *Which object was found at home by the most/fewest children?*

p78 DRAW A SYMMETRICAL PATTERN

Learning outcome
- Begin to recognise line symmetry.

Lesson context
Demonstrate symmetry and explain the principle of building a matching pattern either side of a horizontal or vertical line. Tell the children to make symmetrical patterns or pictures by folding a sheet of paper in half vertically, then drawing round 2–D shapes. More able children start with a horizontal or diagonal line.

Setting the homework
Use an enlarged copy of the sheet to draw in a few squares.

Back at school
Cut each pattern from the sheet, and mount them.

 p79 SCOOP AND COUNT

MATHS TO SHARE

Learning outcomes
• Give a sensible estimate of at least 50 objects.
• Count reliably up to 100 objects by grouping them: for example, in tens, then in fives or twos.

Lesson context

Estimating and scooping objects

Name	Estimate	Actual number

Copy this chart on to a flip chart. Ask a child to estimate the number of objects that they can scoop up with two hands from a large tub. Write the estimate on the chart, then let the child try. Ask the child to group the objects into piles of ten and group any ones left over into small groups. Ask the child to count the total by touching and counting each pile. Let the children carry out a similar activity in groups.

Setting the homework
Make sure the children understand how to estimate, scoop and count as they have done in school.

Back at school
Scribe the children's results on a class chart. Ask: *Who made the closest estimate to the actual number? Who estimated a number that was too few/too many?*

 p80 COUNTING ON AND BACK 3

MATHS TO SHARE

Learning outcome
• **Describe and extend simple number sequences:** count on and back in steps of 3 from any given number

Lesson context
On a 0–99 chart, colour the 'zero', '3' and '6' squares for the pattern of 'count on 3'. Write the sequence of 'count on 3' underneath: 0 → 3 → 6. Tell the children to copy and continue the pattern and the number sequence on their own grids. More able children can 'count back 3' from 98.

Setting the homework
Show the children the sheet and check that they understand it. For children who are only confident with numbers up to 30, tell them to ask their Helper to write different numbers between 10 and 30 in the middle boxes.

Back at school
Look through each child's work. For children who had difficulties, plan further work using a printed number line.

p81 COUNTING IN TENS TARGETS

MATHS TO SHARE

Learning outcome
• **Describe and extend simple number sequences: count on or back in tens, starting from any two-digit number.**

Lesson context
Give each child a set of 11–20 number cards. The children should turn over one card and write down that number. They continue to count on in tens from that number, writing the numbers until a 'nineties' number is reached.

Setting the homework
Use the example on the sheet to demonstrate the activity.

Back at school
Look through work for errors. Play a 'count on 10' circle game. Hold up a card from a shuffled 1–19 set and say the number. Children should continue the count until a nineties number is reached.

 p82 100 GAME

MATHS TO SHARE

Learning outcomes
• **Know by heart:** all pairs of multiples of 10 with a total of 100 (e.g. 30 + 70).
• Use patterns of similar calculations.

Lesson context
Write the following patterns on the board:

1 + 9 = 10	10 + 90 = 100
2 + ? = 10	20 + ? = 100
10 – 1 = 9	100 – 10 = 90
10 – 2 = ?	100 – 20 = ?

Tell the children to copy and continue writing the addition patterns, then the subtraction patterns. For more able children, include 100 + 900 = 1000 and 1000 – 100 = 900.

Setting the homework
Show the children the sheet, read out the instructions and check they understand how to play.

Back at school
Plan for the children to play the game with a partner when they have finished other work.

 p83 POSITIONING NUMBERS

MATHS TO SHARE

Learning outcome
• **Order whole numbers to at least 100,** and position them on a number square.

Lesson context
Give each child two copies of a blank 100 grid and some coloured pencils or felt-tipped pens. Use a blank 100 square chart to demonstrate how each child should colour in ten different squares on the grid. Children exchange sheets with a partner and write in the correct numbers on the grid to match the positions of the coloured squares on their partner's grid. Challenge pairs of more able children to colour 20 squares. Have complete 0–99 grids for children who require support.

Setting the homework
Show the children the sheet and check they understand it.

Back at school
Review the activity using a blank 100 square teaching chart. Say numbers between 0 and 99 and ask different children to write the numbers in the correct positions on the square.

p84 QUICK CHANGE

MATHS TO SHARE

Learning outcome
• Add three small numbers by putting the largest number first, and/or find a pair totalling 10.

Lesson context
Play 'All change'. Use a set of 1–30 cards and three different-coloured hoops. Sit the children in a semi-circle with the hoops in a line. Give a card to each child. Choose three children and ask them each to stand in a hoop and show their card. Choose a child to say the total of the three numbers shown. If he or she answers correctly, then they change place with the child in the first hoop. Choose another child to say the new total. If correct, they change places with the child in the second hoop, and so on.

Setting the homework
Read out the instructions and demonstrate the game.

Back at school
Repeat 'All change'. Plan for the children to play the homework game with a partner when they have finished other work.

 **p85 ADD AND SUBTRACT 9** PRACTICE EXERCISE

Learning outcome
• Add/subtract 9: add/subtract 10 and adjust by 1.

Lesson context
Demonstrate the pattern of add/subtract 9 on a 0–99 chart. Point to different numbers and choose a child to say the 'add 9' number. Repeat with 'subtract 9'. Give each child a 0–99 grid, a small cube and paper. Tell the children to throw the cube on the grid, and write down the number it lands on followed by the 'add 9' number.

Setting the homework
Show the children the sheet and make sure they understand it.

Back at school
Look through each child's work and comment. Play a mental 'add 9' game: say a number and choose a child to add 9 to it each time.

p86 £5.00 PROBLEM INVESTIGATION

Learning outcomes
• Recognise all coins. Find totals and work out which coins to pay.
• Use mental addition and subtraction to solve simple problems in 'real life' involving money.

Lesson context
Get the children to find ways to make £5.00 with coins.

Setting the homework
Show the children the sheet and check that they understand it.

Back at school
Copy the chart from the homework sheet. Choose children to give results. Ask if anyone has the answer to Gran's £7.00 problem.

 **p87 QUICK MULTIPLICATION GAMES** MATHS TO SHARE

Learning outcome
• **Know by heart: multiplication facts for the 2 and 10 times tables.**

Lesson context
Use a 0–99 chart to demonstrate how to colour in the pattern of 'counting in 10s' up to 20. Write the 10 times table (both ways) underneath:

$0 \times 10 = 0$ $10 \times 0 = 0$

$1 \times 10 = 10$ $10 \times 1 = 10$

Tell the children to copy and continue the pattern of 10s and the multiplication statements. Encourage more able children to continue the tables beyond 10 × 10.

Setting the homework
Show the children the sheet and check they understand it.

Back at school
Play the homework activity as a class game. Hold up a card and choose a child to multiply the number on the card by 2 or by 10.

p88 DOUBLE A DOUBLE PRACTICE EXERCISE

Learning outcomes
• **Understand the operation of multiplication as repeated addition.**
• Derive quickly: doubles of all numbers to at least 15.

Lesson context
Give each group a set of dominoes and some paper. Tell the children to select one, add up the number of spots and add that number to itself and then multiply the number of spots by 2. Use a flip chart to demonstrate recording the answers.

Setting the homework
Demonstrate how to carry out the activity.

Back at school
Look through the work for errors and comment.

p89 SHOP FOR SWEETS GAMES AND PUZZLES

Lesson outcome
• Use mental addition, subtraction and simple multiplication to solve simple problems involving numbers and money in 'real life'.

Lesson context
Demonstrate 'Shop for sweets with £2.00'. Let the children work in pairs. Give each pair a spotted dice and a copy of the following chart:

Shop for sweets with £2.00			
Sweet	Price	Number to buy	Total cost
Chews	1p		
Jelly mice	2p		
Mini lollies	3p		
Candy sticks	4p		
Nut crisps	5p		
Choc bars	10p		
	Totals		
		Change from £2.00	

One child throws the dice to see how many to write in the first row of the 'Number to buy' column. The pair work out the 'Total cost' for those sweets. The other child throws the dice for the next sweet and so on. At the end, both children work out the total cost of all the sweets and the change from £2.00.

Setting the homework
Explain that the children will be re-playing 'Shop for sweets', but each player is to fill in their own sheet. Provide extra copies of page 89 as needed.

Back at school
Encourage the children to play the homework version of the game with a partner.

 **p90 QUICK DOUBLE AND HALF GAMES** MATHS TO SHARE

Learning outcomes
• **Know by heart: doubles of all numbers to 10 and the corresponding halves.**
• Begin to recognise and find one half of shapes.

Lesson context
Draw two 4 × 4 square grids on the board. Demonstrate two different ways to colour half the squares in the grid (8). Ask the children to draw similar 4 × 4 square grids on squared paper and find more ways to colour half the squares in each grid.

Setting the homework
Show the children the sheet and check that they understand it.

Back at school
Repeat the double and half homework games with the whole class.

p91 MEASURE UP
MATHS TO SHARE

Learning outcome
- **Estimate, measure and compare lengths using standard units** (m, cm).

Lesson context
Copy this chart on to the flip chart:

Less than 3 metres	About 3 metres	More than 3 metres

Children take turns to pace out 3m from an agreed start line. Mark each child's estimate with a beanbag. Choose two children to measure the distances with three metre sticks. Allow 10cm more or less as 3m. Each child writes their name in the appropriate column of the chart.

Setting the homework
Read out the instructions and ask a child to help you measure the length of a long item to the nearest metre or centimetre, using a tape measure or 1m length of string.

Back at school
Review the homework activity with the class. Make lists of items the children measured, giving their estimates and the actual lengths to the nearest metre. Discuss the results in terms of the longest/shortest item, and the closest estimate to the actual measurement.

p92 DOMINO DIVIDES
PRACTICE EXERCISE

Learning outcomes
- Derive quickly: division facts corresponding to the 2 times table.
- Use the ×, ÷ and = signs to record mental calculations in a number sentence.

Lesson context
Give each child a shuffled pile of even numbered 2–20 cards, placed face down, and a dice marked with ×2 and ÷2 to play 'Times 2/divide by 2'. Each child turns over one card, throws the dice and writes a number statement. For example, for the 4 card and a dice showing ×2, a child would write 4 × 2 = 8. Less able children may use interlocking cubes if they require help.

Setting the homework
Use the example given to demonstrate the activity.

Back at school
Play 'Times 2/divide by 2'. Look through the homework for any errors. Children who found the work difficult may require work with dividing numbers by 2 using interlocking cubes.

p93 FOOD TRAIL
MATHS TO SHARE

Learning outcome
- **Compare masses using standard units** (kg, g).

Lesson context
Give each group ½kg and 1kg weights and a pan balance. Make a copy of this chart for each group:

Less than ½kg	About ½kg	Between ½kg and 1kg	More than 1kg

First, let the children handle the weights. Each child chooses an object they think weighs about ½kg and takes a turn to balance the object and write its name in the correct column.

Setting the homework
Plan for this homework activity to be carried out during a weekend. Check the children understand. Tell them to take a notebook and pencil to write down the weights.

Back at school
Copy the homework chart on to the board and ask the children to give you their information. Ask the children to name the heaviest/lightest item and any items with the same weight.

p94 SWEET SORT
INVESTIGATION

Learning outcome
- Solve a given problem by sorting, classifying and organising information in simple ways; such as: in a table; in a block graph.

Lesson context
Copy the tally chart below onto the board, drawing a simple picture of each type of liquorice allsort in the first column. Include a row for 'dislike all'. Make a copy of the chart for each child.

Sweet	Number	Total
Dislike all		

Tally and total how many children like each type of allsort. Ask questions about the results: *How many tally marks did the most/least favourite allsort get?* Ask the children to copy the results of the class tally chart on to their chart. Tell them to use 2cm squared paper to make a graph by drawing pictures of each type of allsort under the columns of squares and then to colour one square for each tally mark alongside/above each picture.

Setting the homework
Explain that the children are to sort and record the contents of a packet of assorted sweets.

Back at school
Cut the charts from the sheets, mount and create a wall display.

p95 TELLING THE TIME
PRACTICE EXERCISE

Learning outcome
- Read the time to the hour, half hour and quarter hour on an analogue clock.

Lesson context
Make a sheet of clocks with a clock stamp and copy one sheet for each child. Use a teaching clock to demonstrate 'quarter past' and 'quarter to'. Give each group a set of 12 cards showing times quarter past the hour and 12 cards showing quarter to the hour and the clock sheets. Each child takes a card, copies the time underneath a clock on the sheet and then draws the hands on the clock at that time.

Setting the homework
Show the children the sheet and check that they understand it.

Back at school
Look through the work and identify errors. Children who found telling the time to the half and/or quarter hours difficult may require further help.

 **TWO-WAY COUNTS** PRACTICE EXERCISE

Learning outcome
• **Describe and extend simple number sequences:** count on and back in steps of 4 and 5.

Lesson context
Demonstrate colouring the pattern of counting in 4s up to the number 8 (missing out three numbers) on 0–99 chart, writing the number sequence underneath 0 → 4 → 8 → ? Give each child a 0–99 grid to copy and continue the pattern and number sequence. Repeat for 5s.

Setting the homework
Explain how the children are to count on/back 4 from each number in the first column and 5 in the second column.

Back at school
Note any child who worked only with numbers 10–25. Congratulate those who tried 'Count on/count back 6'.

p97 COUNTING ON GAME MATHS TO SHARE

Learning outcome
• **Describe and extend simple number sequences:** count on in steps of 1 to 5 and 10 from any given small number.

Lesson context
Design a worksheet showing the first two numbers of different number sequences. Include counting on and back in steps of 1 to 5 and 10: 24 → 26 → [ ] → [ ] → [ ] → [ ]. Make a copy for each child.

Setting the homework
Show the children how to count on from the starting number to the finishing number using the stars to keep track of the count.

Back at school
Decide the rule and choose a child to start. Each child takes a turn to say the next number until a 'nineties' number is reached.

p98 ADDING THREE NUMBERS MATHS TO SHARE

Learning outcome
• **Use knowledge that addition can be done in any order to do mental calculations more efficiently.** For example: add three small numbers by putting the largest number first and/or find a pair totalling 10.

Lesson context
Give each group a box of dominoes and some paper. Spread the dominoes out face down. Tell the children to select three dominoes each time and record the total number of spots on each. Then they should arrange their three numbers to add them putting the largest first and/or finding a pair totalling 10.

Setting the homework
Demonstrate how the game is to be played.

Back at school
Plan for the children to play the game with a partner or small group.

p99 FIND THE DIFFERENCE PRACTICE EXERCISE

Learning outcome
• Find a small difference by counting up from the smaller to the larger number.

Lesson context
Each group should spread a box of dominoes out face down. Each child should select one domino, draw round it, mark in the spots, and then write a difference sentence underneath; e.g., for a 2/6 domino, write '2 ← 4 → 6'.

Setting the homework
Demonstrate how the children are to do the task.

Back at school
Look through each child's work and comment.

p100 FOUR IN A ROW GAMES AND PUZZLES

Learning outcome
• **Order whole numbers to at least 100,** and position them on a number square.

Lesson context
Shade in 20 individual squares on a blank 100 square and make a copy for each child. Demonstrate how each child should write the correct numbers on to another blank grid for the positions shown by the shaded squares on their other grid.

Setting the homework
Use playing cards, Ace to 9, and a 0–99 chart. Demonstrate the game. Cross out numbers rather than using counters.

Back at school
Let the children play the game with a partner.

p101 ADD/SUBTRACT 19 AND 21 GAMES MATHS TO SHARE

Learning outcome
• Begin to add/subtract 19 and 21: add/subtract 20 and adjust by 1.

Lesson context
Demonstrate on a 0–99 chart the pattern of adding and subtracting 19 from a given number. Give each child a 0–99 grid, a cube and paper. Demonstrate how to throw the cube on to the grid, write down the number it lands on, then write the 'Subtract 19/Add 19' numbers. Tell them children to complete 20 statements.

Setting the homework
Use an enlarged 0–99 grid and playing cards to explain how the children are to carry out the activity.

Back at school
Play 19/21 games with the class. Say a number and choose a child to add 19 each time: *My number is 27, Rosie your number is… ?* Repeat with 'Subtract 19'.

p102 DIFFERENCE PATTERNS INVESTIGATION

Learning outcomes
• Add/subtract 9 and 11: add/subtract 10 and adjust by 1.
• Begin to add/subtract 19 and 21: add/subtract 20 and adjust by 1.

Lesson context
Give each group a set of numeral cards 40–60 and paper. Tell them to spread the numeral cards out on the table, select a card and write the number down. Now add 11, then 21, to the number, recording like this: 42 → 53 → 74. Ask the children to do this ten times, then repeat with the rule 'Subtract 21, then subtract 11'. Provide 0–99 grids for those who need support.

Setting the homework
Demonstrate the activity using the example given on the sheet.

Back at school
Look through work for errors and comment. Review the work as a class activity. With a 0–99 chart, invite the children to point to two numbers with a difference of 9, 19, 11 or 21 each time.

p103 TRIOS

INVESTIGATION

Learning outcome
• Begin to add three two-digit numbers with the help of apparatus.

Lesson context
Give each group a set of 10–30 numeral cards. Tell them to use the numbers to find different ways to add three numbers. Write an example of an addition with three two-digit numbers on the board and demonstrate how to add them by grouping and adding the tens, then the units, and then finding the total, for example: $23 + 34 + 11 \rightarrow 60 + 8 = 68$. Show how they are to record answers by drawing round a triangle template on their sheet, writing a number beside each corner and writing the total inside the triangle each time. Provide Cuisenaire rods or interlocking cubes for children who may require support.

Setting the homework
Demonstrate how the children are to complete the sheet.

Back at school
Look through the work for errors. Note any child who needs help. Encourage children to work out totals mentally.

p104 SUBTRACTING 'TEENS' NUMBERS

INVESTIGATION

Learning outcome
• Use known number facts and place value to subtract mentally.

Lesson context
Copy the following subtraction patterns on to the board:

$26 - 13 =$ $27 - 14 =$ $28 - 15 =$ $29 - 16 =$
$36 - 13 =$ $37 - 14 =$ $38 - 15 =$ $39 - 16 =$
46... etc. (Continue each pattern up to a 'sixties' number.)

Use an example to demonstrate how to subtract by counting back 10 from the larger number, then counting back the units. For example, $35 - 12 \rightarrow 25 - 2 = 23$. Ask the children to copy and complete the subtractions on the board. Encourage more able children to continue writing each subtraction pattern up to a 'nineties' number. Provide 0–99 grids for children who require additional support. Go on to try patterns starting:

$24 - 16 =$ $25 - 7 =$ $27 - 19 =$

Demonstrate how to subtract by counting back 10 from the larger number, then counting through the 'tens' number.

Setting the homework
Demonstrate how the children are to complete the work.

Back at school
Look through work for errors and comment. Note any child who may need further work. Encourage the children to work out totals mentally whenever appropriate.

p105 SHOPPING WITH £5.00

PRACTICE EXERCISE

Learning outcome
• Use mental addition and subtraction to solve simple problems involving money, using one or two steps.

Lesson context
Design a worksheet similar to the homework sheet showing six to eight different items costing between 50p and £3.50. Make a copy for each child. Ask the children to suggest two different items that can be bought with £5.00 and work out the change needed. Show the children how to record the activity. Less able children may buy only one item each time and use coins to work out the change. Challenge more able children to shop with £10.00, choosing three items.

Setting the homework
Read out the name and cost of each item and tell the children what they are to do. Tell children who bought only one item or worked with £10.00 in class to do the same at home.

Back at school
Review the work with the class. Choose children to read out a list of items bought for you to write on the board. Let the class work out the money spent and the change.

p106 TREASURE HUNT

GAMES AND PUZZLES

Learning outcome
• Give instructions for moving along a route in straight lines and round right-angled corners: for example, to pass through a simple maze.

Lesson context
Use 2cm squared paper to draw a grid 6 x 8 squares. Design a treasure map similar to the one on the homework sheet, using pictures and names of features in a village such as: school, pond, house, tower, church, shop, tree and a gate. Plot a twisting route from the gate to the treasure and write it as an arrow code (as on the homework sheet) underneath the map on the master sheet. Copy the sheet for each child. Demonstrate the activity. Less able children can work with a partner.

Setting the homework
Tell the children to find the hidden treasure by following the arrow instructions as they have done in school.

Back at school
Use an enlarged copy of the map and ask children to draw a line on the map to show where each consecutive instruction moves them. The treasure is at the castle.

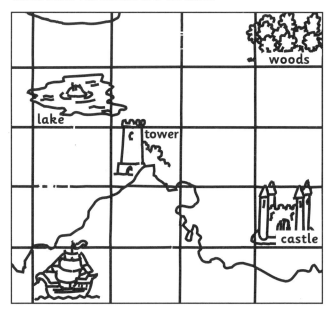

p107 KNOCK DOWN NINE-PINS

MATHS TO SHARE

Learning outcomes
• Solve mathematical problems or puzzles. Suggest extensions by asking ' What if...?' or 'What could I try next?'
• Give instructions for moving along a route in straight lines and round right-angled corners: for example, to pass through a simple maze.

Lesson context
Use 30cm rulers to mark out both sides of the route of a simple maze for a floor robot, with right-angles, left and right turns and a dead end. List and demonstrate the commands for backwards, forwards, or take a quarter turn left or right. During each child's turn at driving the robot, encourage improving the accuracy of each command in relation to the distance to travel. Scribe estimates on the flip chart until the correct commands are found for each section of the route. Write the final sequence of commands on the chart.

Setting the homework
Demonstrate how the children are to play the game with their Helper and how to keep a record of the directions given and the results. The children will need squared paper too.

Back at school
Plan for the children to play the game with a partner when they have finished other work.

p108 MAKING CARROT AND ORANGE SOUP

MATHS TO SHARE

Learning outcome
• Use and begin to read the vocabulary related to mass and capacity.

Lesson context
Make a copy of the following chart for each child:

Name of objects	Estimate	Actual result

For each group you will need: a pan balance, a 100g weight and six sets of small objects for balancing. Each child in the group estimates how many of one type of object will balance 100g and then takes a turn to balance one of the sets of objects against the 100g weight. The children write their results on their chart and compare and discuss their results.

Setting the homework
Show the children the activity sheet and read out the instructions. Emphasise that they must ask their Helper to supervise the use of a hob, electrical appliances and pouring hot liquids.

Back at school
Prepare some small circles of plain paper. Draw a large chart on a sheet of paper with two columns headed 'Liked' and 'Disliked'. Tell the children to make a 'happy' face from their paper circle if they liked the soup; a 'sad' face if they didn't. Stick the faces on the chart. Ask: *What is the difference between the number of children who liked and disliked the soup?* Display the completed chart.

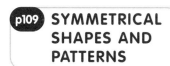

p109 SYMMETRICAL SHAPES AND PATTERNS

INVESTIGATION

Learning outcome
• Begin to recognise line symmetry.

Lesson context
Explain that for a letter to be symmetrical, both halves have to be the same shape, like a reflection in a mirror. Offer examples with vertical, horizontal and diagonal lines of symmetry and a non-symmetrical letter. Ask the children to draw around letter templates and then test if the letters are symmetrical by drawing lines to cut them in half.

Setting the homework
Show children the sheet and check that they understand it.

Back at school
Choose children to name a symmetrical item they found at home. Cut out the chart of each child's work and display them.

p110 COUNT BACK, COUNT ON

PRACTICE EXERCISE

Learning outcome
• **Describe and extend simple number sequences;** count on and back in steps of 1 to 5 and 10 from any given small number.

Lesson context
On a 0–99 chart, demonstrate colouring the pattern and writing the sequence of counting on in steps of 3 from 4 underneath. For example: 4 → 7 → 10 → 13 → ? Give each child a 0–99 grid and ask them to copy and continue the pattern and sequence up to a 'nineties' number. Repeat using a different colour for the pattern of count back 3 from 99, again writing the sequence underneath.

Setting the homework
Demonstrate with a 0–99 chart, cube and dice (marked 1–5 and 10).

Back at school
Look through each child's work and comment. Note any child who needs further work counting on and back.

p111 DOUBLE IT, HALVE IT

MATHS TO SHARE

Learning outcome
• Derive quickly: doubles of multiples of 5 to 50; halves of multiples of 10 to 100.

Lesson context
Write 5 → 10 → 15 → 20… → 50 on the board. Ask the children to copy each number and then write its double, for example 5 → 10. Repeat with the sequence of counting on 10 to 100, but writing the halves. Have Cuisenaire rods or interlocking cubes available for children who need support.

Setting the homework
Demonstrate how to play the games by holding up a suitable number card and choosing a child to say the answer.

Back at school
Play the homework games as a class game with a set of cards using multiples of 5–50 and multiples of 10–100. Hold up one card each time and choose a child to answer. Where a number ends in 5, the number is doubled. Where a number ends in 0, it is halved.

p112 COUNTING BACK GAME

MATHS TO SHARE

Learning outcome
• **Describe and extend simple number sequences:** count back in steps of 1 to 5 and 10 from any given small number.

Lesson context
Design a worksheet showing the first two numbers of different number sequences using counting on and back in steps of 1 to 5 and 10, e.g.: 36 → 32 → [ ] → [ ] → [ ] → [ ]. Make a copy for each child to complete.

Setting the homework
Show the children how to count back from the starting number to the finishing number using the stars on the sheet to keep track of the count.

Back at school
Repeat the homework activity as a class circle game. Hold up a card, decide the rule and choose a child to start the count. Each child takes a turn to say the next number in the sequence until zero or a 'ones' number is reached.

p113 HUNDREDS AND THOUSANDS

MATHS TO SHARE

Learning outcomes
• **Know by heart:** all pairs of multiples of 10 with a total of 100.
• Use patterns of similar calculations.

Lesson context
Write the following number statements on the board:

1 + 9 = 10	10 + 90 = 100	100 + 900 = 1000
2 + ? = 10	20 + ? = 100	200 + ? = 1000
10 − 1 = 9	100 − 10 = 90	1000 − 100 = 900
10 − 2 = ?	100 − 20 = ?	1000 − 200 = ?

Ask the children to copy and continue the addition, then subtraction, patterns by working across the page. Allow less able children to complete all the addition and subtraction facts for 10, then 100, and then 1000.

Setting the homework
The children will also need copies of Resource photocopiable page 28. Use drawings of the cards on a flip chart and the example shown to demonstrate the rules of the game.

Back at school
Let the children play the game with a partner or small group.

p114 DOMINO SUBTRACTION

PRACTICE EXERCISE

Learning outcome
• Use known number facts and place value to subtract mentally.

Lesson context
Ask the children to select two dominoes, draw them, then write the two-digit numbers denoted by the spots underneath each domino. Tell the children to count a blank on a domino as 0 units not 0 tens. They should write the larger number first and use the easiest method to carry out the resulting subtraction.

Setting the homework
Explain that they will be practising subtracting two-digit numbers using dominoes as they have been doing in school.

Back at school
Look through the work for errors.

p115 PAY AND CHANGE FROM £5.00
PRACTICE EXERCISE

Learning outcome
• Recognise all coins. Find totals, give change, and work out which coins to pay.

Lesson context
Give each pair a set of three money dice: two marked 2p, 5p, 10p, 20p, 50p, £1.00 and one marked £2.00, £2.00, £1.00, £1.00, 50p, 50p; and some coins. Copy the following chart:

Spend and change from £5.00			
Money spent in coins	Total	Change in coins	Total change

Pairs take turns to roll the dice to determine the total money spent. Both write the amount on the chart, by drawing round coins. Next they work out the total change, writing the amount and drawing the change in coins. Able children can use four dice and carry out the activity as 'Pay and change from £10.00'.

Setting the homework
Tell the children they will be practising paying money and finding the change from £5.00. Explain that they are to try to draw the change using the least number of coins.

Back at school
Plan for the children to repeat the activity with a partner.

p116 SUBTRACTION GAME

MATHS TO SHARE

Learning outcome
• Use known number facts and place value to subtract mentally.

Lesson context
Write subtraction patterns on the board from a 'thirties' to a 'seventies' number:

36 – 23 =   37 – 24 =   38 – 25 =   39 – 26 =
46 – 23 =   47 – 24 =   48 – 25 =   49 – 36 =
56 – 23... up to 76 – 23... etc.

Use the flip chart to demonstrate the method of subtracting the tens and then the units of the smaller number, for example: 36 – 23 → (36 – 20), then 16 – 3 = 13. Ask the children to copy and complete the subtractions on the board. Challenge the more able children to continue each pattern up to a 'nineties' number.

Setting the homework
Show the children the sheet and read the instructions. They have to carry out the subtractions by putting the larger number first and then use the easiest method to find the answer. Use the examples in the Helper's notes to remind the children of different methods.

Back at school
Play the game with the class using a set of 10–100 cards. Hold up two cards. Choose a child to subtract the smaller from the larger number.

p117 5 TIMES TABLE

MATHS TO SHARE

Learning outcome
• Begin to know: multiplication facts for the 5 times table.

Lesson context
Use a 0–99 chart and a flip chart to demonstrate colouring the pattern of 5s to 100 and write the 5 times table facts (both ways) underneath, for example:

0 x 5 = 0   5 x 0 = 0
1 x 5 = 5   5 x 1 = 5
2 x 5 = 10...   5 x 2 = 10...

Ask the children to copy and continue the pattern and the 5 times table on to their own 0–99 grids, as far as possible or to 100.

Setting the homework
Demonstrate how to use a paper clip as a spinner, and how to play the game.

Back at school
Recite the 5 times table together. Then ask the class quick-fire questions such as: *What are two fives?...six fives?* and so on.

p118 DOUBLE AND HALVE
PRACTICE EXERCISE

Learning outcome
• **Know and use halving as the inverse of doubling.**

Lesson context
Spread out a set of even numbered cards, 20–50, face up on each table. Each child selects a number to write on their sheet, then writes the halved number to the left and the doubled number to the right each time, for example: 18 ← 36 → 72. Less able children can use Cuisenaire rods or interlocking cubes to help.

Setting the homework
Copy the grid and a recording space from the sheet and demonstrate.

Back at school
Look through the work for errors. Play a mental 'double and halve' game where you say an even number between 20 and 50 and a child doubles or halves the number.

p119 DOMINO MULTIPLICATION
PRACTICE EXERCISE

Learning outcomes
• **Understand the operation of multiplication as repeated addition.**
• Check with an equivalent calculation.
• Use known number facts to add and multiply mentally.

Lesson context
Use a box of dominoes for each group. Demonstrate how the children should select and draw round a domino, mark in the spots and then write two multiplication and corresponding repeated addition statements for the domino each time. For example, for the 4/2 domino:

4 x 2 = 8   4 + 4 = 8
2 x 4 = 8   2 + 2 + 2 + 2 = 8

Explain how each multiplication statement can be translated into a repeated addition: 4 x 2 is 'two lots of four' or 'four add four'. Tell the children to write statements for at least ten dominoes. Have interlocking cubes available to help less able children.

Setting the homework
Explain that they will be working with dominoes to practise multiplication and repeated addition.

Back at school
Look through the work for errors. Note any child needing to practise writing multiplication and corresponding repeated addition statements.

p120 SUPER SAVER   INVESTIGATION

Learning outcome
- Use addition and subtraction to solve simple problems in 'real life' involving money.

Lesson context
Make a set of ten cards showing pictures, names and prices of items, such as: Book 60p, Pens 90p; CD £4.00; Watch £6.00; Game £1.00; Note pad 30p; Camera £12.00; Comic 50p; Trainers £40.00; Personal stereo £60.00. Then make a copy of the following chart for each child:

Half price sale		
Item	Full price	Sale price
Pens	90p	45p

Demonstrate to the children how to complete the sheet by writing down the information and then working out the sale price.

Setting the homework
Show the children the sheet and read instructions. Emphasise that they must do the activity with their Helper. They do not have to do the activity straight away. Suggest that they try to complete it at a weekend.

Back at school
Ensure that all children have been given sufficient time to carry out the homework task before you review. Copy the chart from the sheet on to the board and choose different children to give their results. Ask the children to name the item on the chart where the most/least money would be saved.

p121 MULTIPLY AND DIVIDE BY 2 GAME   MATHS TO SHARE

Learning outcomes
- **Know by heart: multiplication facts for the 2 times table.**
- Derive quickly: division facts corresponding to the 2 times table.

Lesson context
Use a flip chart to demonstrate writing the pattern of multiplying and dividing even numbers by 2, for example:

$2 \times 2 = 4$ $2 \div 2 = 1$
$4 \times 2 = 8$ $4 \div 2 = 2$
6... etc.

Tell children to copy and continue the patterns up to 30 × 2. For more able children, offer the full range of odd and even numbers to 30, introducing the use of remainders in division, for example:

$2 \times 2 = 4$ $2 \div 2 = 1$
$3 \times 2 = 6$ $3 \div 2 = 1 r 1$
4... etc.

Challenge them to continue writing the patterns.

Setting the homework
Write examples on the board using odd and even numbers to demonstrate which are to be multiplied or divided by 2.

Back at school
Play the game with the class using numeral cards 1–20. For each card, choose a child to multiply or divide the number by 2 depending on whether the number is odd or even.

p122 FOUR IN A LINE   GAMES AND PUZZLES

Learning outcomes
- **Know by heart: multiplication facts for the 2 and 10 times tables.**
- Begin to know: multiplication facts for the 5 times table.

Lesson context
Repeat the previous 'Lesson context' (for page 121), but developing the pattern of multipling and dividing by 10.

Setting the homework
Show the children the homework activity sheet and read out the instructions. Use an enlarged copy of the grid on the sheet with a pack of cards, Aces to 10s, and a dice marked 2, 2, 5, 5, 10, 10 to explain and demonstrate the rules of the game.

Back at school
Plan for the children to play the game with a partner when they have finished other work.

p123 SHOP FOR FRUIT   MATHS TO SHARE

Learning outcome
- Use mental addition, subtraction and simple multiplication to solve simple problems involving numbers and money in 'real life'.

Lesson context
Make a copy of the following chart for each pair of children. Several pairs should work together in each small group.

Multiple shopping with £10.00			
Item	Price	Number to buy	Total cost
Marble	10p		
Pokémon card	20p		
Book	30p		
Model kit	40p		
Beanie toy	50p		
	Totals		
		Change from £10.00	

Use a copy of the sheet and a dice to demonstrate the game. One child throws the dice to see how many to write in their 'Number to buy' columns. Both children work out the 'Total cost'. The second child throws the dice for the next item and so on. When all the items have been bought, both children work out the total cost of all the toys bought and the change from £10.00. Find out which pair bought the most items and which pair had the most change from £10.00.

Setting the homework
Make extra copies of the homework sheet (page 123) for the children to take home. Tell the children they will be playing 'Shop for fruit' at home in the same way as the game in class, but, that they do not play with partners. Each player throws the dice and writes down their score each time.

Back at school
Look through the homework for errors. Let the children play the game with a partner when they have finished other work.

p124 PLANNING A PICNIC

Learning outcome
• Begin to recognise that four quarters make one whole.

Lesson context
Demonstrate on the flip chart how to divide circles into halves and quarters, leaving one circle whole. Label the fractional parts. Do the same with squares. Ask children to fold, cut and paste circles in the same way as they have been shown, labelling each part. Repeat the activity with squares.

Setting the homework
Show the children the sheet and read out the instructions. They do not have to do the activity straight away. Suggest that they plan their picnic at a weekend. Tell them they will be asked afterwards about who they invited and where they went to eat it, and what flavours of sandwich fillings, crisps, drinks and types of fruit they chose.

Back at school
Ensure that all children have been given sufficient time to carry out the homework task. Choose children to describe how they prepared the picnic. Ask questions about quarters of the items the children ate, such as: *Four packets of crisps – what fraction of that number is one packet ..two packets ..three packets?* Try making different class graphs in another session, e.g.: 'Different types of sandwich filling used'.

p125 QUARTERING A SQUARE PUZZLE

Learning outcomes
• Begin to recognise that four quarters make one whole.
• Solve mathematical problems or puzzles. Suggest extensions by asking 'What if…?' or 'What could I try next?'

Lesson context
Draw two 4 x 4 square grids on the board. Demonstrate two different ways to colour a quarter (4) of the squares. Ask the children to draw similar grids on squared paper and find different ways to colour a quarter of the squares in each grid. Challenge them to find at least nine different ways.

Setting the homework
Show the children the sheet and read out the instructions. Emphasise that they must divide each grid into four quarters, colouring each quarter a different colour.

Back at school
Draw some 4 x 4 grids on a flip chart. Choose different children to colour a solution on each grid. Look through the work for any errors and comment.

p126 HOW MUCH TIME?

Learning outcome
• Use units of time and know the relationships between them.

Lesson context
Copy the following time facts on to a flip chart:

60 seconds = 1 minute	60 minutes = 1 hour
24 hours = 1 day	7 days = 1 week
4 weeks = 1 month	12 months = 1 year

Write some 'How many?' questions on the board for the children to answer: *...days in two weeks? ...days in four weeks? ...weeks in two months? ...weeks in five months? ...weeks in ten months? ...months in two years? ...minutes in half and one hour? ...seconds in half a minute?* Read through the time facts with the children, then ask them to copy and complete the questions.

Setting the homework
Draw the month wheel from the homework sheet on the board and use an example of a child's birthday to demonstrate. Be sensitive to Jehovah's Witness children who may not celebrate birthdays.

Back at school
Look through the work for errors.

p127 TRAVELLING TO LONDON BY TRAIN

Learning outcomes
• Solve simple problems involving numbers in 'real life', money and measures.
• Read the time on a 12-hour digital clock.

Lesson context
For each group, provide a set of time cards to the hour, half hour and quarter hour in digital form, such as 3.15; 2.30; 6.45 and so on. Prepare and photocopy a sheet of clock faces for each child. Use a clock stamp. Demonstrate reading and recording times in digital form. Ask the children to complete the sheet by selecting a card, drawing the hands on a clock to show the time and then writing the time underneath. Use sets of cards showing minutes past the hour in five-minute intervals for more able children, such as 2.25; 6.10; 8.50 and so on.

Setting the homework
Show the children the sheet and read out the instructions. Emphasise that they must carry out the task with their Helper.

Back at school
Ensure that all the children have been given sufficient time to carry out the homework task. Copy the charts from the sheet to the board and choose a child to report their results. Ask questions about the results, with a show of hands, e.g.: *Who planned to travel from... station? A different station? Who planned to catch a train at the same time? A different time?*

p128 MAIL SORT

Learning outcome
• Solve a given problem by sorting, classifying and organising information in simple ways, such as: in a simple table; in a block graph.

Lesson context
Use a flip chart to write down the times the children go to bed, earliest to latest. Take a count of hands and write the number against each bed-time. Demonstrate how to make a graph on squared paper, drawing the axes with a ruler, writing the bed-times listed on the flip chart along the bottom of the chart and the numbers of children on the left-hand side. The children should use the results on the flip chart to make a graph on 2cm squared paper, colouring one square for each child above each bed-time. Draw the graph outline on squared paper for those unable to do it for themselves.

Setting the homework
Set the children to carry out the homework during one week. Show the children the sheet and read out the instructions.

Back at school
Copy the chart on the homework sheet on to the board and choose a child to name an item of mail and the number that were delivered to their house in one week. Scribe the results on the chart. Ask the children to name the item of mail with the most/fewest number and any items with the same number. Repeat with different children.

0-99 number square

0	1	2	3	4	5	6	7	8	9
10	11	12	13	14	15	16	17	18	19
20	21	22	23	24	25	26	27	28	29
30	31	32	33	34	35	36	37	38	39
40	41	42	43	44	45	46	47	48	49
50	51	52	53	54	55	56	57	58	59
60	61	62	63	64	65	66	67	68	69
70	71	72	73	74	75	76	77	78	79
80	81	82	83	84	85	86	87	88	89
90	91	92	93	94	95	96	97	98	99

This page can be copied for use for number square activities, or enlarged to at least A3 and photocopied on to card, or on to paper and laminated, to be cut up into individual numeral cards to use with the activities in this book.

Tens and hundreds cards

10	20	30	40	50
60	70	80	90	100
100	200	300	400	500
600	700	800	900	1000

This page can be copied on to card, or on to paper and laminated, to be cut up into individual numeral cards to use with the activities in this book.

Name:

Counting and writing numbers

You will need: a pencil, crayons or felt-tipped pens.

Read these instructions with your Helper.

- Count from 0 to 49.

- Write the numbers in order on the grid.

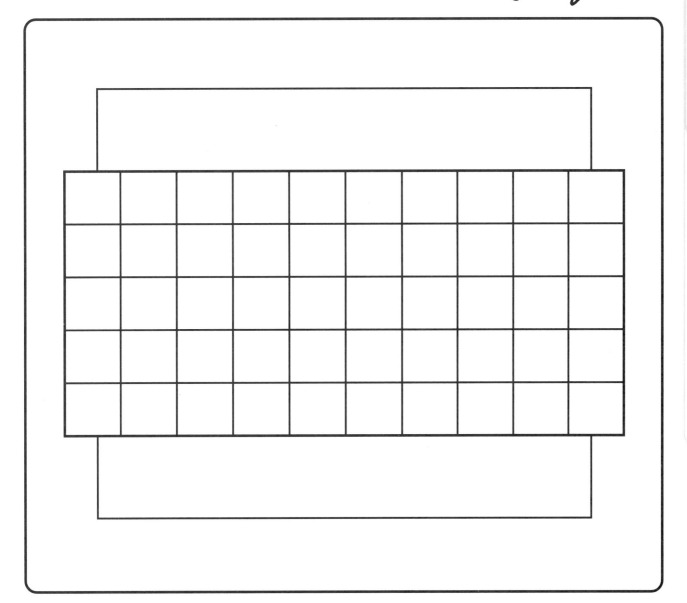

- Decorate the border with a number pattern.

Dear Helper,

This activity is to help your child to practise counting and writing numbers in order up to 49. To get started, ask your child to complete the first two lines up to 19. Check that the numbers are correctly written before they complete the other lines in the grid. If your child has difficulty completing the grid by themselves, make a note of the last number they were able to write without help. Offer guidance with completing the rest of the grid. Challenge your child further by repeating the activity, but this time ask your child to start at 49 and count down to 0 (or as far as possible without help).

NUMBERS AND THE NUMBER SYSTEM

COUNTING AND NUMBER PROPERTIES

Counting objects on a tray

You will need: a tea tray and a pencil, different sets of objects in tubs ranging from 10 to 50 items.

Read these instructions with your Helper.

- Tip one set of objects on to the tray and group the objects into piles of ten and ones left over.

- Find the total by counting on in tens, then adding on the ones left over.

- Write your answers on the chart. Ask your Helper if you need help with writing the name of the objects.

- Repeat with the other sets of objects.

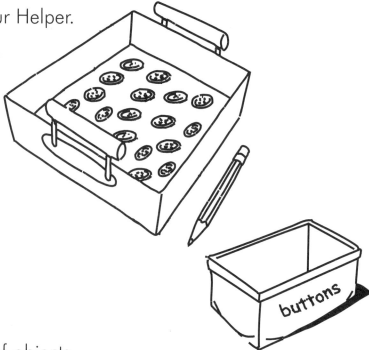

Name of objects	Total number

Dear Helper,

This activity is to help your child to count large numbers of objects using the method of grouping objects in tens. Encourage your child to touch each pile of ten as they count and say: *10, 20...* etc.. Check the total is correct before the answer is written on the chart. If your child has difficulty with counting objects above 20, reduce the number of items in each set to between 10 and 20. Encourage your child to count and group ten items together, then count on the remaining ones saying: *10, 11, 12...* and so on.

Name:

Counting on in ones

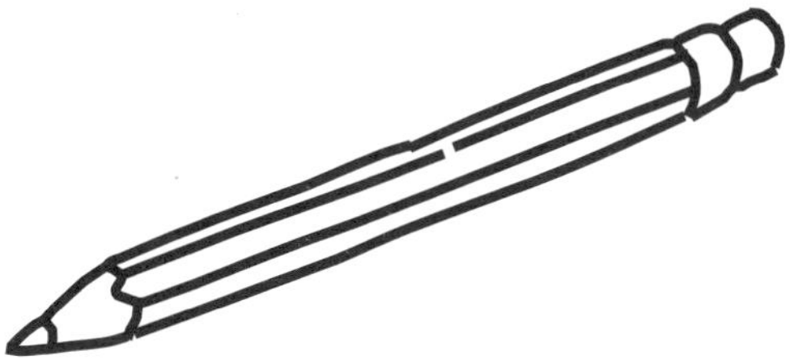

You will need: a pencil.

Read these instructions with your Helper.

- Ask your Helper to say a number between 1 and 50.

- Write down the number in the first box.

- Count on in ones and write the numbers to the end of the line.
  If the number said is 21, you would write:
  21, 22, 23, 24... and so on.

- Repeat to complete the sheet.

Dear Helper,

This activity is to help your child to count on in ones from any number between 1 and 50. Start by saying a number between 1 and 10 for the first line, then use higher numbers for the other lines. If your child has difficulty with counting and writing numbers above 20, write different numbers between 1 and 10 in the first box of each row for your child to start from. To challenge your child further, increase the range of numbers you say up to 90.

Counting on and back in ones

You will need: 0–99 number square, a small cube and a pencil.

Read these instructions with your Helper.

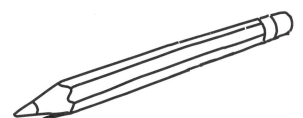

- Throw the cube on the square.

- Write the number it lands on in the first centre box.

  ◯ ← 23 → ◯

- Count back 1 and write the number in the left-hand circle.

- Count on 1 and write the number in the right-hand circle.

- Repeat to complete the sheet.

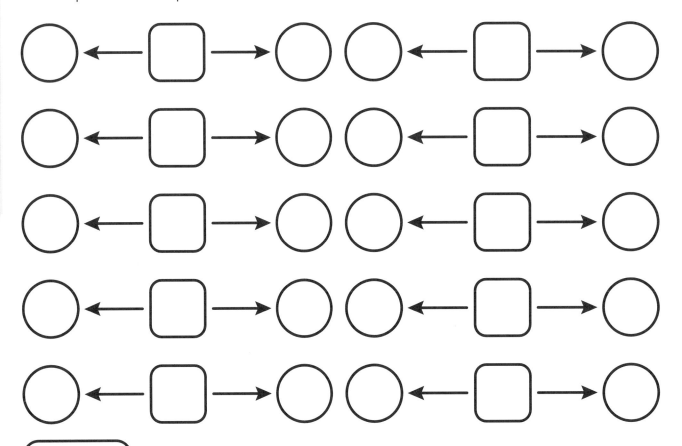

PHOTOCOPIABLE

Dear Helper,

This task is to help your child to practise counting on and back in ones from any number between 0 and 99. If your child has difficulty working with numbers above 20, write different numbers between 1 and 19 in the middle boxes for them to count from, instead of using the number square and cube. To challenge your child further, repeat the activity with the rule 'counting on and counting back 2'. Try 'counting on and counting back 10'.

Name:

10 game

You will need: a shuffled set of playing cards, Ace to 10 from a pack.

Read these instructions with your Helper.

- Ask your Helper to show you a card.

- What number would you have to add to the number on the card, to make 10? Work the answer out in your head.

If the card shown is:

You would say: 6

- If you are correct, your Helper gives you the card.

Dear Helper,

This game is to help your child learn by heart all the pairs of numbers that make 10 when added together. Play the game slowly at first, then quicken the pace. Try playing the game against the clock. How many cards can your child win in 1 minute? If your child has difficulty with the game, encourage them to work out the answer by counting on from the number on the card using fingers. To challenge your child further, play the game where the number on the card has to be subtracted from 10 and your child says the number left each time.

PHOTOCOPIABLE

33

Name:

Adding two numbers

How many addition sums can you write using two of these numbers?

| 1 | 2 | 3 | 4 | 5 |
| 6 | 7 | 8 | 9 | 10 |

I have written ☐ sums.

Dear Helper,

In this activity your child is practising combining two numbers to find a total. Make sure they:
- write down the numbers putting the larger number first, e.g., for 2 and 6 write 6 + 2 = 8
- add the second number by counting on from the first, e.g., for 8 + 3 say: 8, 9, 10, 11.

If your child has difficulty with finding totals above 12, encourage them to work with numbers 1–6 only.
To challenge your child further, suggest making addition sums using three numbers.

100 MATHS HOMEWORK ACTIVITIES • YEAR 2 TERM 1

Name:

Tens and units

You will need: 0–99 number square, a small cube, a pencil and red and blue coloured pencils or felt-tipped pens.

Read these instructions with your Helper.

- Throw the cube on the square. Write the number it lands on in the box under the first abacus.

- Draw beads on the abacus spikes to show the number of tens in red and units in blue.

For **32** use

```
●      ●
●
●
┌─────┐
│ 32  │
└─────┘
```

- Repeat to complete the sheet.

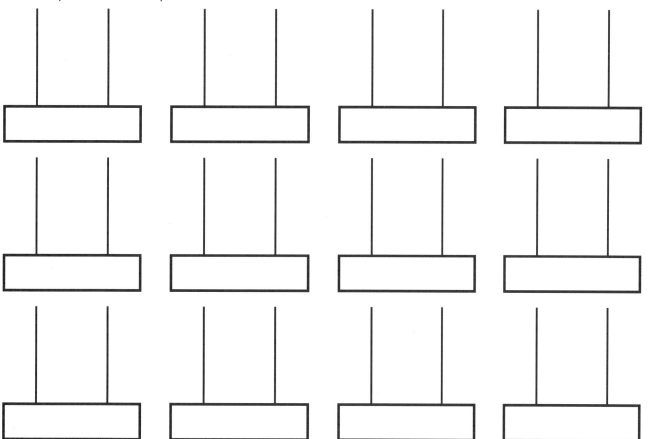

Dear Helper,

This task is to help your child to know what each digit in a two-digit number represents in tens and units. If your child has difficulty working with numbers above 30, write different numbers between 10 and 30 in the boxes underneath each abacus for your child to draw in the beads. Challenge your child by playing a game where you say a number as tens and units, for example, '3 tens and 4 units' and your child says the whole number, 'Thirty-four.'

Name:

Doubling numbers

Read these instructions with your Helper.

10	3	7	4	15
12	5	13	1	9
2	8	14	11	6

- Choose a number from the grid and write it in the first box.

- Double the number and write the answer in the second box.

  For 3, write

3	6

- Draw an 'H' beside any doubles box you complete in your head.

- Repeat until nine numbers have been used.

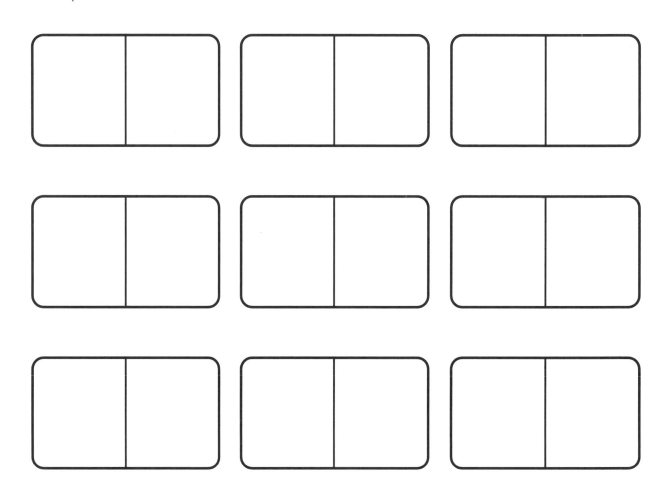

Dear Helper,

This task is to help your child to practise doubling numbers so that they begin to know them by heart. Encourage your child to double numbers in their head where possible, but to use fingers or write workings underneath the box, if they are unsure. If your child has difficulty doubling numbers above 10, suggest that they use numbers 1 to 10 from the grid. Encourage your child to draw numbers higher than 5 as spots, then count the spots twice to find the doubled number: for 6, draw ⚅ 12. To make the activity more challenging, tell your child to use only numbers 6 to 15.

Name:

Target 50p

A game for two or more players. First player with a 50p in the centre wins.

You will need: a spotted dice and a shaker. Each player will need a copy of the board and ten 1p coins, five 10p coins, one 50p coin.

Read these instructions with your Helper.

- Each player throws the dice and places that number of 1p coins on the outside ring.

- When there are ten 1p coins, change them for a 10p coin, placed in the inside ring.

- Five 10p coins can be changed for the 50p coin.

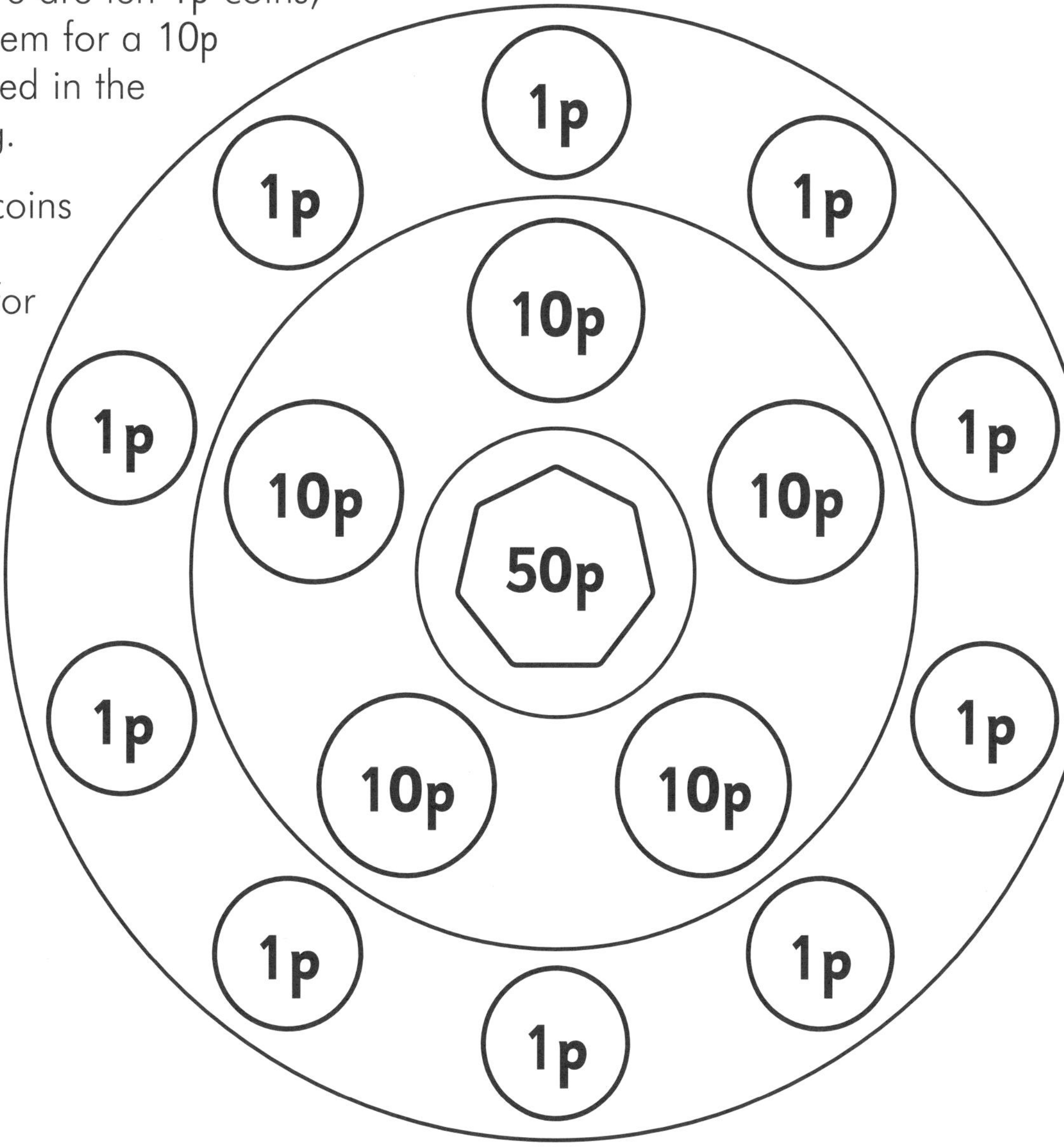

Dear Helper,

This game is to help your child to recognise equivalent values between coins; that ten 1p coins can be changed for one 10p coin and five 10p coins can be changed for one 50p coin. Repeat the game for practice. To challenge your child further, ask them to say the total amount of money on the board after each turn.

Name:

Adding two 'teens' numbers

Read these instructions with your Helper.

15	11	17
12	18	14
19	13	16

- Choose two numbers from this grid and write them as a sum in the first box. Put the larger number first. For 12 and 14, write 14 + 12.

- Split each number into tens and ones. Write the tens in the top boxes and the units in the bottom boxes of the drawing.

For **14 + 12** write:

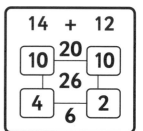

- Find the total of the tens and units separately, then add the numbers together and write the total in the centre.

- Repeat to complete the sheet.

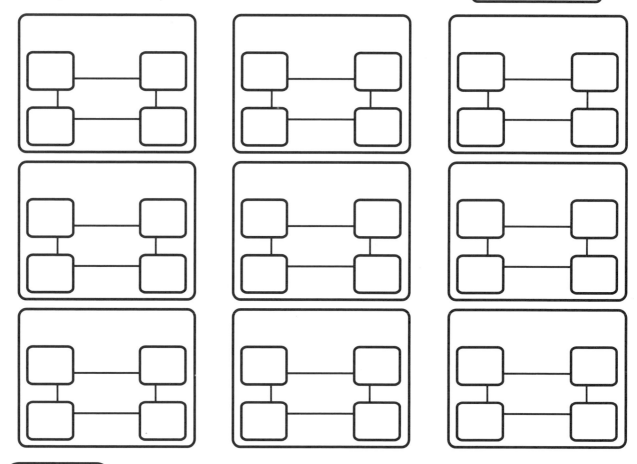

Dear Helper,

This activity is to help your child to add two 'teens' numbers together mentally by splitting the numbers into tens and units, then adding the totals together. If your child has difficulty adding pairs of numbers above 15, encourage your child to work with numbers 11 to 15 only.
To challenge your child further, draw the following extra grid for your child:
Ask your child to choose one number from both grids to add together each time.

27	21	26
22	29	25
24	28	23

100 MATHS HOMEWORK ACTIVITIES • YEAR 2 TERM 1

Name:

20 game

You will need: a shuffled set of 1–20 number cards.

Read these instructions with your Helper.

- Ask your Helper to show you a card.

- What number would you have to add to the number on the card to make 20? Work the answer out in your head.

If the number shown is: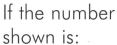

You would say: 4

- If you are correct, your Helper gives you the card.

Dear Helper,

This game is to help your child learn by heart all the pairs of numbers that make 20 when added together. Play the game slowly at first, then quicken the pace. Try playing the game against the clock. How many cards can your child win in 1 minute? An easier version of the game is to play a '10 game' with cards 1–10 where your child says a number to make 10 each time. A more difficult version is for your child to subtract the number on the card from 20 and say the number left each time.

Add and subtract 10

You will need: a 0–99 number square, a small cube and a pencil.

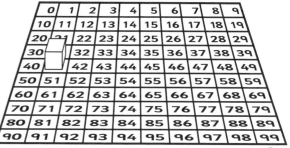

Read these instructions with your Helper.

- Throw the cube on the square.

- Write the number it lands on in the first centre box.

- Subtract 10 from the number in your head and write the answer in the left-hand circle.

- Add 10 to the number in your head and write the answer in the right-hand circle.

- Repeat to complete the sheet.

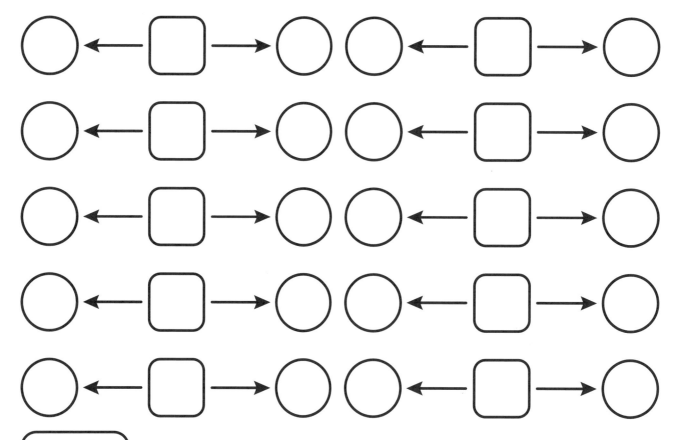

Dear Helper,

This task is to help your child to mentally add and subtract 10 from any two-digit number up to 99. If your child is unsure about adding snd subtracting 10 mentally, encourage them to use the number square to 'count on' and 'count back' 10 in ones until the 'add/subtract 10' pattern is recognised. To challenge your child further, change the rule to 'Add and subtract 20'.

Name:

£1.00 problem

You will need: a pencil and some 1p, 2p, 10p, 20p and 50p coins.

Read these instructions with your Helper.

- Find five different ways to make £1.00.

- Draw and label your chosen coins on the money boxes.

Dear Helper,

This activity is to help your child recognise and combine coins to make totals. Encourage your child to check the total each time by counting on from the coin with the highest value. For 50p, 20p, 20p and 10p, say: *50p and 20p is 70p; 70p and 20p is 90p; 90p and 10p is £1.00.* If your child is unsure of combining coins to make £1.00, encourage them to count out ten 10p coins, then exchange the 10p coins for other coins. Challenge your child further by including £1.00 coins and repeating the activity as 'ways to make £1.50', then £2.00. Ask: *which way uses the fewest coins?*

Name:

Estimating and measuring length

You will need: a ruler marked in centimetres, a pencil and a set of six small objects of different lengths, such as a pen, a paperclip, a nail, a book, a fork and a box.

Read these instructions with your Helper.

- Write the name of each object as a list in the first column of the chart. Ask your Helper if you need help with spelling the names.

- You and your Helper look at each object in turn and write your estimate of its length on the chart. (You write your estimate first.)

- You use a ruler to measure the length of each object to the nearest centimetre (or $\frac{1}{2}$cm). Ask your Helper to check the measurement before you write the result on the chart.

Name of object	Estimates in cm		Actual length	Order in size; shortest to longest
	You	Helper		

Dear Helper,

This activity is to help your child to make sensible estimates of the length of small objects in centimetres and to measure objects accurately to the nearest centimetre (or ½cm). After completing the measuring, discuss each result with your child. Now ask your child to place the objects in a line in order of size, shortest to longest and number the objects in order 1st – 6th on the chart. If your child is not familiar with measuring to the nearest ½cm, encourage them to record results as '2 and a bit cm'. Challenge your child further by repeating the activity with a different set of objects.

Name:

Measure up

You will need: a tape measure marked in centimetres and a pencil.

Read these instructions with your Helper.

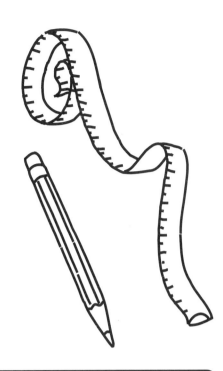

- Take turns with your Helper to measure each other using a tape measure.

- Start by measuring the length of each other's hand in centimetres to the nearest centimetre. Write the results on the chart. Ask your Helper to measure your hand first before you measure your Helper's hand.

- Do the same with each item on the chart.

	Me	**Helper**
Length of hand		
Length of foot		
Around the wrist		
Around the head		
Length of arm		
Length of leg		

Dear Helper,

This activity is to help your child to use a tape measure to measure length in centimetres. After completing the measuring, ask your child to look at the results and find the longest and the shortest measurement. Help your child if they have difficulty with reading the numbers on a tape measure. Challenge your child further to find the pairs of measurements that are closest together and furthest apart in distance. Can your child work out the difference in centimetres between each pair of measurements?

SHAPE AND SPACE | MEASURES, SHAPE AND SPACE

Hunt for circles and spheres

You will need: a pencil, crayons or felt-tipped pens and a book or clipboard to rest the sheet on.

Read these instructions with your Helper.

- Search round your house for objects that are shaped like circles or spheres.

- Draw, colour and write the name of each object you find on the chart. Ask your Helper if you need help with spelling the names of objects.

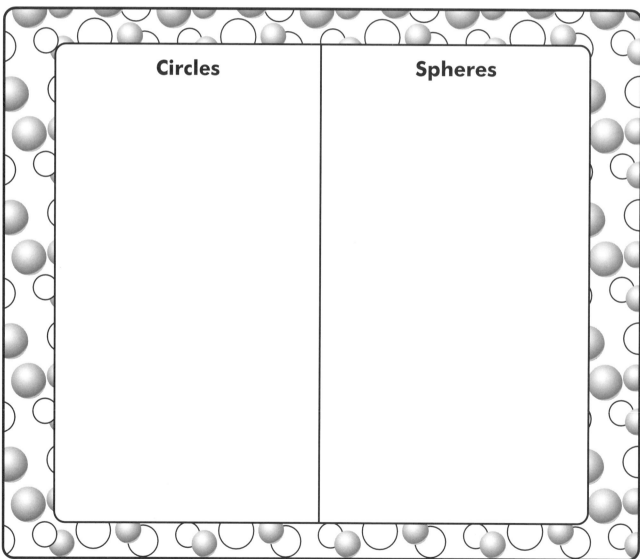

Circles	Spheres

Dear Helper,

This activity is to help your child to recognise circles and spheres that can be found in familiar objects around the home. Allow your child to start looking for shapes by themselves and then let them show you the objects they found. Draw your child's attention to objects they have not noticed, for example: *Can you find a circle on the cooker?* or *Can you find a sphere in the fruit bowl?*

Name:

Shapes made from five squares

You will need: a sheet of newspaper, a ruler marked in centimetres, a pencil, crayons or felt-tipped pens.

Read these instructions with your Helper.

- Ask your Helper to measure and cut out five newspaper squares **4cm** by **4cm**.

- Arrange the five squares in a shape so that at least one side of one square is against one side of another square: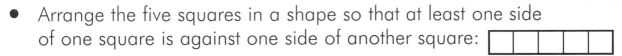

- Draw and colour the shape you have made on the grid below using one square on the grid for each newspaper square.

- Find other ways to arrange the five squares and draw them on the grid too.

Dear Helper,

This activity is a well-known mathematical puzzle to help children find different solutions by trying out ideas. Encourage your child to find at least six solutions. If your child has difficulty copying the shapes to the sheet, give them a plain sheet of paper, a pile of 4 x 4cm newspaper squares and some adhesive. Tell them to make up a shape with five squares on the paper, then paste the squares in place each time. Challenge your child to find the 12 possible solutions (shapes which are the same but facing a different way do not count!).

COUNTING AND NUMBER PROPERTIES | **NUMBERS AND THE NUMBER SYSTEM**

My number / your number games

Read these instructions with your Helper.

- Count to 50 in ones.

  Your Helper says: 1, you say: 2,
  your Helper says: 3, and so on.

Play these games in the same way.

- Count to 100 in tens.

- Count to 20 in twos.

- Count down from
  50 in ones.

- Count down from
  100 in tens.

- Count down from
  20 in twos.

Dear Helper,

These games are to help your child learn by heart the number sequences of counting forwards and backwards in ones, tens and twos. Play the games slowly at first, then quicken the pace until the sequence can be said as quickly as possible. Vary the games by asking your child to say the first number each time. If your child gets stuck, continue counting from that point saying each number together. Repeat the count once more for practice. Challenge your child by extending counting in ones to 100, in tens to 200 and in twos as far as possible or up to 100.

PHOTOCOPIABLE

Name:

Odd and even dominoes

You will need: a box of dominoes and a pencil.

Read these instructions with your Helper.

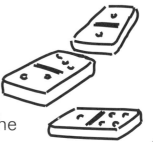

- Spread the dominoes out face up on a table.

- Find a domino where the total number of spots on the domino equals one of the numbers in the grid below.

- Decide whether the number is odd or even, draw the spots on a blank domino and write the total beside it.

- Repeat until a domino has been drawn for each number in the grid.

Odd **Total**

6	9	1	4
3	10	7	12
8	2	11	5

Even **Total**

- Write all the odd and even numbers in order from smallest to largest.

Odd numbers

Even numbers

PHOTOCOPIABLE

MENTAL CALCULATIONS + AND –   CALCULATIONS

Scoring 12 with three cards

You will need: a pack of playing cards (Ace to 10) and a pencil.

Read these instructions with your Helper.

- With your Helper lay out three suits of cards (e.g., spades, diamonds and clubs) in three lines in order Aces to 10s.

- Find different ways to score 12 by choosing one card from each line.

- Pick up the cards you select and place them in the easiest order for you to add the numbers together. Write your answer as an addition sum on this sheet.

- Put the cards back in the lines after use each time.

Dear Helper,

This activity is to help your child to find different solutions to a number problem by trying out ideas. Encourage your child to find ten or more solutions. An easier version of the problem is to use three suits of playing cards, Ace to 6. A more challenging version is to use four suits of playing cards, Ace to 10 for your child to find different ways to score 15 with four cards (one from each line).

Name:

Rounding numbers

You will need: 0–99 number square, a small cube and a pencil.

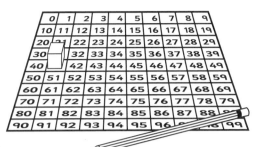

Read these instructions with your Helper.

- Throw the cube on the square.
  Write down the number the cube lands on.

- Round the number up or down to the nearest ten.
  For 42 write 42 → 40. For 79 write 79 → 80.

Dear Helper,

Your child has been learning in school how to round numbers to the nearest ten. This task gives your child an opportunity to practise this. If your child is unsure about rounding numbers, draw a red line vertically down the number square after all the numbers ending in 4 to help them. Tell your child that numbers before the red line are rounded down and numbers above are rounded up to the next ten. Carry out the activity against the clock to make the activity more challenging. How many numbers can your child complete in 1 minute?

Name:

Ordering numbers

You will need: a shuffled pack of 1–30 number cards and a pencil.

Read these instructions with your Helper.

- Ask your Helper to deal out five cards, placing them face up in a line.

- Arrange the cards in order from the lowest to the highest number. Ask your Helper to check that the order is correct before you write your answer on the sheet.

- Collect the cards and place them at the bottom of the pack before your Helper deals five more cards.

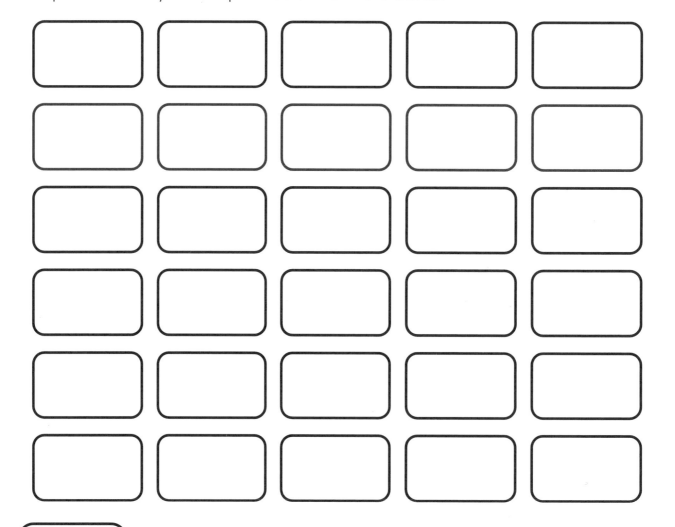

Dear Helper,

This activity is to help your child to place numbers in order of size using the range of numbers 1–30. An easier version is to use a shuffled pack of 1–20 cards. Challenge your child further by asking them to draw a ring around all the odd numbers in each line.

Name:

Adding three numbers

You will need: three spotted dice and a pencil.

Read these instructions with your Helper.

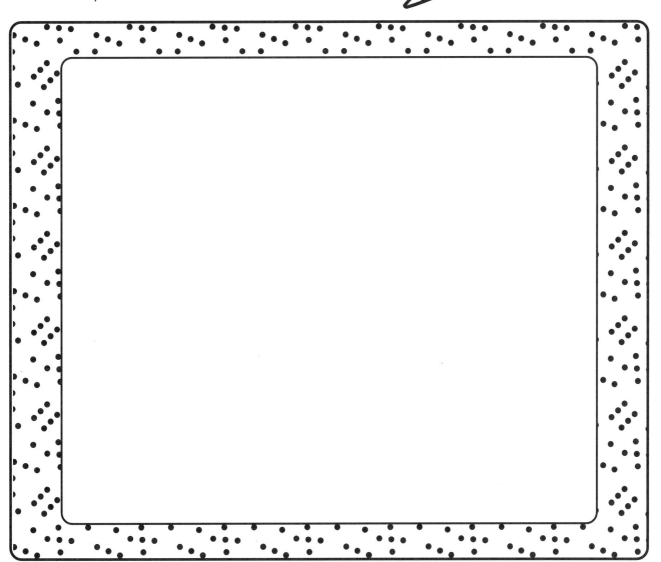

- Throw the three dice. Find the total score in your head by putting the larger number first or finding a pair of numbers that total 10.

- Write your answer as an addition sum.

Dear Helper,

This task is to help your child practise finding the total of three small numbers mentally by adding the numbers together in the easiest order to find the total. Encourage your child to play the game against the clock. How many sums can be written in 5 minutes? Offer help by asking: *Which is the largest number?* or *Can you find two numbers that make 10?* If your child gets stuck with the addition, encourage them to count on from the largest number in ones using the spots on the other dice. Challenge your child to use four dice instead of three, and add four numbers each time.

PHOTOCOPIABLE

51

Name:

Pay and change from 50p

You will need: a pencil and some 1p, 2p, 5p, 10p and 20p coins.

Read these instructions with your Helper.

- Choose three amounts from the boxes below, add them together and write the total in the 'Pay' column.

- Work out the change from **50p** and write the amount in the 'Change' column.

- Draw the amount of change in money using the least number of coins.

- Repeat to complete the sheet.

| 1p | 2p | 5p | 10p | 20p | 20p |

Pay	Change	Change in the least number of coins

Dear Helper,

This activity is to help your child to add amounts of money and work out what the change will be from 50p in the least number of coins. If your child needs help, guide them to find the amount paid by putting the larger amount first, then to count the change using 10p and/or 1p coins. For 25p paid say: *25p and 10p makes 35p, and another 10p makes 45p, and 5p makes 50p. So the change is: 10p + 10p + 5p = 25p.* Then convert the change to the least number of coins: 20p and 5p. A harder version is to draw another box marked 50p and include 50p coins for your child to find change from £1.00.

Name:

Footwork

You will need: a large pile of 2p coins, a pencil and sheets of plain paper.

Read these instructions with your Helper.

- Ask your helper to draw around your foot on a sheet of paper.

- Cover the picture of your foot with 2p coins and count the coins in twos: '2p, 4p, 6p...' and so on, to find out how much your foot is 'worth'.

- You draw around your helper's foot on paper and do the same.

- Try this with other members of your family. Write a sentence for each person.

My foot is worth ☐ p

_____ foot is worth ☐ p

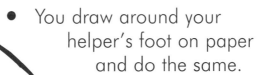

Dear Helper,

This activity is to help your child to practise counting in multiples of 2 to find a total. If your child needs help with counting the coins, encourage them to move each coin to outside the foot outline on the sheet as it is counted. Join in with counting the coins if your child gets stuck. Challenge your child to find out how much two feet are 'worth' by doubling the number. Ask your child to find the difference in 'worth' between your foot and theirs by removing the number of coins their foot is 'worth' from yours and counting the remaining coins in twos.

Domino multiplication

You will need: a box of dominoes and a pencil.

Read these instructions with your Helper.

- Recite the two times table to your Helper.

- Discard the double six and six/five dominoes, then spread the dominoes out face down on a table.

- Pick up a domino and draw a picture of the domino on the sheet.

- Count the total number of spots and multiply that number by 2.

  For  write 5 × 2 = 10.

- Repeat to complete the sheet.

Dear Helper,

This activity is to help your child to use facts from the two times table to help them multiply a number by 2 mentally. If your child is unsure of the two times table, encourage them to place a 2p coin for every spot on the domino in a line and count in twos to find the total, saying: '2, 4, 6...' etc. Challenge your child to repeat the activity and multiply the number of spots on each domino by 10.

Hand work

Read these instructions with your Helper.

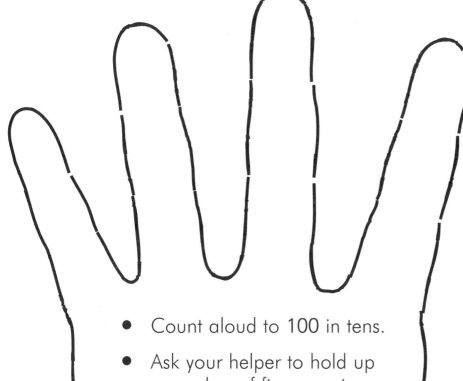

- Count aloud to 100 in tens.

- Ask your helper to hold up a number of fingers using two hands. Each finger is worth 10.

- You count the fingers in tens and say the total.

- Say the number needed to add to the total to make 100.

Dear Helper,

This activity is to help your child to practise counting in multiples of 10 to find a total, then find the number needed to make a total of 100. If your child needs help with this activity, let your child touch each finger you hold up as they count in tens, then count the knuckles of the folded down fingers in tens to find the number needed to make 100. A variation of the activity is to ask your child to start with 100 and then subtract the 'finger values' 10 at a time. Can they say how many tens make up the number left?

Name:

£1.00 to spend at the paper shop

Birthday card 25p	Eraser 5p	Comic 30p	Felt-tipped pens 75p	Activity book 60p	Pencil 10p

- Choose two items to buy.
- Find the total cost.
- What change will you get from £1.00?
- Try this four more times.

Items	Cost	Change

Dear Helper,

This shopping activity is to help your child to practise addition of money to find the total cost and work out the change from £1.00. If your child gets stuck, encourage them to make each amount in 10p and / or 1p coins and then count the amount in tens adding on any remaining ones. Ask your child to find the change by counting on from the total cost to £1.00 in 10ps and 1ps. To challenge your child further, ask them to buy three items each time.

Name:

Ways to halve a pizza

You will need: a large cardboard circle cut into eight equal pieces to represent slices of pizza and some crayons or felt-tipped pens.

Read these instructions with your Helper.

- Make up the whole 'pizza' on a table.

- Count the slices and tell your Helper how many slices make one half of the pizza.

- Carefully remove half the slices and count how many slices are left.

- Look at the positions of the remaining slices and draw them in the same places on the first pizza picture.

- Make up the pizza again before trying to halve the pizza in another five different ways.

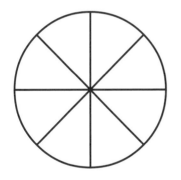 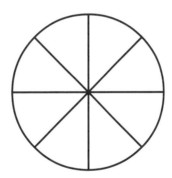 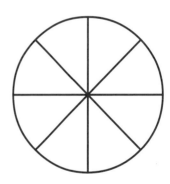

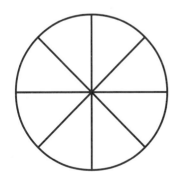 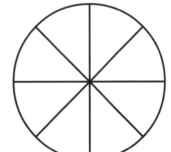 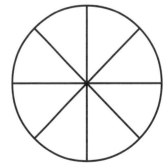

Dear Helper,

This activity is to help your child to recognise that when a simple shape is divided into an even number of equal-sized pieces that these pieces can be put in any position to make up one half of a whole shape, for example ⊛. To help your child understand this principle, encourage them to put the four slices that are removed together in a conventional half circle ⊖ each time. To challenge your child further, try a variation of the activity using a 12 egg box and six eggs. Ask your child to place the six eggs in different positions in the egg box. Use the back of the sheet to draw some 6 × 2 grids ▦ for your child to record the results.

Name:

Baking cakes

You will need: a mixing bowl and spoon, a fork or whisk, a non-stick 12-bun baking tray, a cake rack and kitchen scales.

Read these instructions with your Helper. Then work together.

Ingredients

   2 eggs

   100g soft margarine

   100g sugar

   100g flour

   2 tablespoons of milk

What to do

- Pre-heat oven to 170°C or Gas Mark 5.

- Cream the margarine and sugar together in a bowl.

- Add two eggs and beat into the mixture.

- Add the flour and milk.

- Beat to make a creamy mixture.

- Spoon the mixture into the bun tin and bake for **15** minutes.

- Helper, please remove cakes from oven and place on a rack to cool.

Dear Helper,

This activity is to help your child to use units of mass/weight in a real-life situation by baking some cakes. Help your child to measure out the ingredients accurately and supervise them preparing the mixture for cooking. When the cakes are cooked, you remove them from the oven and place them on a rack to cool. Challenge your child further by following other recipes. Choose recipes from a simple cookery book such as Jane Suthering's *Children's Quick and Easy Cookbook* (published in UK by Dorling Kindersley). IMPORTANT NOTE: As the kitchen is a potentially dangerous environment (hot liquids, electrical appliances and sharp objects), make sure that you supervise your child throughout this activity.

Name:

Ball games

You will need: a football-sized ball.

Ask your Helper to play these 'throw and catch games' with you.

- Your Helper throws the ball to you.

- You catch the ball and say: 'Monday', then throw the ball back.

- Your Helper throws the ball to you again. You catch the ball and say: 'Tuesday'.

- Continue until you have said all the days of the week.

- If you drop the ball, you must start again at 'Monday'.

- Repeat the game using the names of months of the year.

Dear Helper,

These games are to help your child learn by heart the names of the days of the week and months of the year. Start by standing a short distance from your child. Play the games slowly at first, then quicken the pace. Make the games more challenging by using a tennis ball and/or increasing the distance between the players. Encourage your child to try these variations of the games on their own.
- Bouncing the ball, saying the name of a day/month for each bounce.
- Throwing the ball against a wall and catching it, saying a name of a day/month each time the ball is caught.

PHOTOCOPIABLE

SOLVING PROBLEMS

ORGANISING AND USING DATA

TV times

You will need: a pencil and a list of today's TV programmes from a newspaper, magazine or teletext.

Read these instructions with your Helper.

* Look through the list of TV programmes for one TV channel.

* Write the names of all the programmes that start on each hour from 3 o'clock to 8 o'clock on the chart.

Name of TV channel _____

Time	Name of TV Programme

My favourite TV programme is _____ .

It starts at _____ .

Dear Helper,

This activity gives your child an opportunity to sort and classify information in a real-life situation.
If your child is unsure how to tackle this activity, write the times as they are written in the listings 3.00 to
8.00 in the first column of the chart. Help your child to find a programme that starts at each time for them
to copy to the chart. Leave a blank if there is not a programme starting on the hour. To challenge your
child further, ask: *What programme starts one hour earlier/later than* _____? Repeat the activity using
the listings from another TV channel.

Name:

Timing games

You will need: a watch with a second hand, a favourite book, sheets of lined paper and a pencil.

Play these games with your Helper:

Writing numbers from 1 as far as possible.

Copying words from a page.

- Ask your Helper to say: 'Ready, steady, go' and to time you for 1 minute.

- Count how many numbers and words you have written.

- Play each game again to see if you can beat your score.

	First Try	**Second Try**
Writing numbers		
Copying words		

Dear Helper,

These games are to help your child to gain some understanding of time in relation to carrying out simple tasks. Easier versions of the games: How many times can your child write down numbers 1 to 10? Write a simple sentence on paper such as 'The cat sat on the mat'. How many times can your child copy the sentence? Try other games such as: How long does it take your child to write their name (first name and family name) 20 times? Or how long does it take for your child to get ready for bed? For this second game, try timing your child each night for a week.

Name:

Hunt for cupboards and drawers

You will need: something to rest this sheet on and a pencil.

Read these instructions with your Helper.

- Write the name of each room in your home in the first column of the chart. Ask your Helper if you need help with spelling the names.

- Count the number of cupboards and drawers in each room. Write your results on the chart.

Room name	Cupboards	Drawers

- Use your results to complete this chart.

	Number	Room name
Most cupboards		
Fewest cupboards		
Most drawers		
Fewest drawers		

Dear Helper,

This task is to give your child an opportunity to sort and classify information in a real-life situation. To simplify the task, ask your child to count cupboards and drawers in the kitchen, sitting room and their bedroom only. Challenge your child to use the first chart to find the total number of cupboards and/or drawers in two rooms. Can your child find the total number of cupboards/drawers in your home?

Name:

Counting and writing numbers 99-0

You will need: a pencil, crayons or felt-tipped pens.

Read these instructions with your Helper.

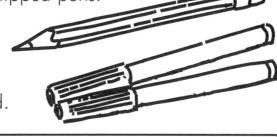

- Count down from 99 to 0 in ones.

- Write the numbers in order on the grid.

- Decorate the border with a pattern.

Dear Helper,

This activity helps your child to practise counting down from 99 in ones and writing numbers in order. Offer guidance if your child has difficulty completing the grid such as writing in the first row from 99 to 90 and 89 at the start of the next row. Challenge your child further by drawing a copy of the grid on the back of the sheet. Ask them to count and write numbers from 100 to 199.

Name:

Odd and even telephone numbers

You will need: a list of telephone numbers of family and friends.

Read these instructions with your Helper.

- Ask your Helper to help you write a list of all your family and friends' telephone numbers.

- Copy the list to the sheet.

- Add the digits of each telephone number and write the totals on the sheet.

- Decide whether the total numbers are odd or even and draw a tick in the correct column.

Name	Telephone number	Total	Odd	Even

Dear Helper,

Leave out area or international country codes. For 0121-111-1234 write 111-1234. For 01234-632541 write 632541. Encourage your child to add the numbers mentally in the easiest order to find the total, starting with the largest number or a pair making 10, then adding the remaining numbers by counting on. If your child finds this difficult, encourage your child to use a separate sheet to re-write each telephone number as individual digits in order of size, starting with the highest digit, then to carry out the addition using fingers or workings if necessary. For example: 632541 as 6 5 4 3 2 1.

Name:

Counting in hundreds

A game for two or more players.

You will need: a spotted dice and shaker.

Each player will need: a copy of the playing board, a set of number cards marked in hundreds 100–1000, a pile of counters (each counter = 100).

Read these instructions with your Helper.

- Start the game by each player laying out a set of number cards in a line in order 100 to 1000 underneath their playing board.

- Each player takes a turn to throw the dice and place that number of counters on any square on the board.

- When the number of counters matches the number of hundreds written on the square, the counters are changed for a matching number card. So, seven counters equals 700.

- The first player with all their number cards on the board wins.

200	900	600	300	500
1000	700	100	800	400

Dear Helper,

This game is to help your child to practise counting in hundreds up to 1000. If your child needs help, encourage them to check numbers of counters during the game by touching each counter and saying: 'One hundred, two hundred...' and so on. Try a harder version without counters. Use two dice with each spot on the dice counting as one hundred. Players can choose whether to throw one or two dice. The score on the dice thrown must equal one of the numbers on the board for a matching card to be placed on a square on the board.

Number squares

You will need: a pencil.

Read these instructions with your Helper.

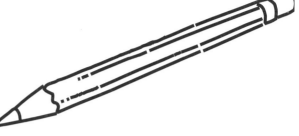

- Write the correct number in each shaded box on the number square.

0									

Dear Helper,

Starting at the zero square, count on along the first row in ones to the first shaded square. Write in the number, then count on again to the next shaded square. Then find the numbers in other rows by counting down the first column in tens then counting along in ones to the shaded square and so on. Challenge your child to write all the numbers they have written in shaded squares on a separate sheet of paper and to round each number to the nearest ten (up or down) writing, for example, 32 → 30 or 58 → 60.

Name:

Target 50

A game for two to four players.

You will need: a set of number cards 1–9, a tray of counters, a score sheet for each player with two columns headed 'tens' and 'ones'.

Read these instructions with your Helper.

- Play the game on a table. Give each player a score sheet. Place the counters in the centre of the table.

- Players take turns to shuffle the cards and deal two cards to each player.

- Each player places one card in each column on their sheet to make a number that is nearest to 50, for example:

- No card can be moved once it is placed.

- Each player says the number they have made. The person with the number nearest to 50 (below or above) takes a counter.

- Put the cards back on the bottom of the pile and deal again.

- Play the game for **5** minutes. The person with the most counters wins the game.

Dear Helper,

This game helps your child to recognise the values of numbers split into tens and ones and to order and compare numbers by value. Encourage your child to be the 'scorer', deciding which number is the nearest to 50 each time. An easier version: Dealer lays down their two cards. Other players have to make a number that is lower in value. Lowest number wins. Try making a number that is higher. A more challenging version: One card is dealt to each player. Players have to decide where to place the card on the sheet before the second card is dealt.

Name:

Change please!

You will need: seven plastic tubs, some 1p, 2p, 5p, 10p, 20p, 50p and £1.00 coins. Use play money if you have some. (Promise to give the coins back!)

Read these instructions with your Helper.

- Make a shopkeeper's till by placing each set of coins in a tub.

- You are the shopkeeper and your Helper is the customer. Your Helper has the tub of £1.00 coins.

- Your Helper says an amount spent, for example: 'I have spent 75p.' They then give you a £1.00 coin and say: 'Can I have my change please?'

- You work out the change from £1.00, sort out the coins you need from the till and count out the change into your Helper's hand, by counting on from the amount spent to £1.00.

- Play this for 5 minutes.

Dear Helper,

This activity provides practise in giving change in coins from £1.00 the shopkeeper's way. Offer guidance to help your child: start from the amount spent, then count coins into your hand up to the next 10p, then go on to use 10p, 20p or 50p coins as appropriate. For example, for 75p spent, say: *75p, 80p, 90p, £1.00*, giving a 5p and two 10p coins. Make the activity easier by starting with multiples of 10p for the amount spent, such as 40p, and then introduce multiples of 5p such as 65p. Make the activity harder by saying all amounts to be under 50p, including amounts such as 31p or 17p.

Name:

Adding two-digit numbers

- Write different addition sums using two numbers from this grid.

19	24	12	27	15
11	21	17	30	28
23	16	20	18	13
22	29	14	26	25

- How many can you complete in 5 minutes?
  Ask your Helper to time you.

I have written ⬚ sums.

Dear Helper,

In this activity your child is practising adding two-digit numbers mentally by splitting each number into tens and ones. Make sure that they:
- write down the larger number first, e.g., for 22 add 27, write 27 + 22.
- add the tens together mentally (20 + 20 = 40), then add the units together (7 + 2 = 9). Finally add both numbers together to find the total (40 + 9 = 49).
Encourage your child to add the numbers mentally where they can, but to write workings if they are unsure. Challenge them further to write addition sums with three numbers.

Name:

Scoring 30 with three cards

You will need: two packs of shuffled 1–20 number cards.

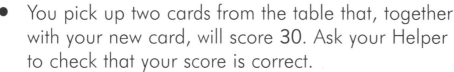

Read these instructions with your Helper.

- With your Helper, lay out one set of cards in four lines of five cards face up on a table.

- Your Helper uses the other pack to deal you one card.

- You pick up two cards from the table that, together with your new card, will score **30**. Ask your Helper to check that your score is correct.

- Replace the cards on the table, placing the dealt card on top of a matching card.

- Continue until all cards have been dealt.

Dear Helper,

This game is to help your child to practise finding three numbers that total 30. Encourage them to work out the number needed with the dealt card to score 30, then to find two cards that make that number. An easier version of the game is to deal two cards for your child to add together, then find a third card to score 30. Challenge them to score 30 with four cards. Where a dealt card has been placed on top of a matching card, the two cards can be picked up and used as double the face value of the card.

Name:

Sorting and counting cash

Read these instructions with your Helper.

- Count the money in your Helper's pocket, purse or wallet each day for three days.

- Sort each type of coin into a pile.

- Count the total amount of money in each pile and write it down on the chart. For example, for three 10p coins, write 30p. Write 0p in any column where there are no coins to count.

- Add together the three amounts in each column to find the total for each type of coin.

	£2.00	£1.00	50p	20p	10p	5p	2p	1p
Day 1								
Day 2								
Day 3								
Totals								

Dear Helper,

This activity is to help your child to sort and count amounts of money in different types of coins and to use a simple chart to write down their results. Help your child count each type of coin if necessary. If your child has difficulty adding three amounts of each coin from the chart, make up each amount for them in coins they find easy to count. Challenge them to use the results from the chart to find the total amount of money in your purse each day.

CALCULATIONS

UNDERSTANDING + AND −

Adding three two-digit numbers

Read these instructions with your Helper.

11	20	16	25	18
26	29	30	12	23
19	15	22	27	14
13	24	28	17	21

- Choose three numbers from the grid and write them as a sum above the first drawing on the sheet, putting the numbers in order with the largest first. For 11 and 22 and 16 write: 22 + 16 + 11.

- Split each number into tens and units. Write the tens in the top boxes and the ones in the bottom boxes of the drawing.

- Find the total of tens and units separately, then add the numbers together writing a sum in the centre of the drawing:

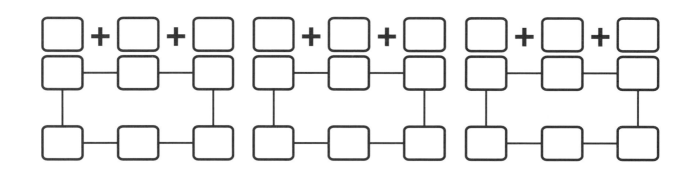

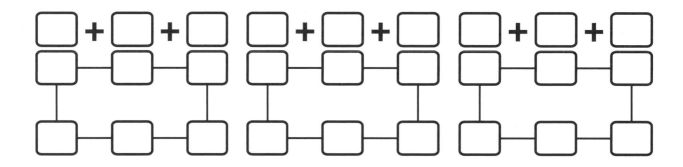

Dear Helper,

This activity is to help your child to practise adding three two-digit numbers by splitting each number into tens and units then adding the totals together. If your child finds this difficult, let your child use 10p and 1p coins to make each number in tens and units before writing the numbers in the drawing. Challenge your child to complete the activity by splitting the numbers into tens and units mentally, only writing the sum in the centre of the drawing each time. Give them another sheet to write some more examples.

Name:

Pay and receive change from £2.00

You will need: a pencil and some 1p, 2p, 5p, 10p, 20p, 50p and £1.00 coins.

Read these instructions with your Helper.

- Choose three amounts from the price tags and write their total cost in the 'Pay' column.

- Work out the change from £2.00 and write the amount in the 'Change' column.

- Draw the amount of change in money using the least number of coins.

£1.00   75p
62p   50p
35p   20p

Pay	Change	Change in the least number of coins

- Repeat to complete the sheet.

Dear Helper,

Encourage your child to:
- add the amounts in the price tags by putting the larger amount first and adding the other two amounts by counting on.
- work out the change by counting on from the total to the next 10p in ones, then in tens to £2.00.
If your child needs help, encourage them to make each amount in coins they are able to count easily, then to find the total. Tell your child to do the same to work out the change. Help them to convert the change to the least number of coins if necessary. Challenge your child by drawing another price tag on the sheet marked £2.00 to allow them to find change from £3.00.

Name:

A special treat

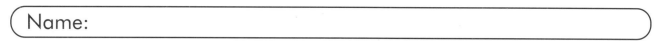

You will need: a notebook and a pencil.

Read these instructions with your Helper.

- Ask your Helper to plan some time to take you to your favourite eating place for a meal. Perhaps you could invite your family or a friend to come too.

- During the mealtime, write down in your notebook what you each chose from the menu and the price of each item.

- Ask your Helper to allow you to pay for the meal with cash and to receive and count the change.

Money paid ☐   Total cost ☐   Change ☐

My meal	Helper's meal

- Back at home, copy the results onto this sheet.

Dear Helper,

This activity is to give your child a real-life experience of choosing and paying for food. Support your child by helping them to write everything down during the mealtime. Extend the activity by including others invited to the meal. Ask your child to use the back of the sheet to write down results for extra persons. Back at home, challenge your child to work out the cost of each meal from the results. Use coins or notes if help is needed.

Name:

Container hunt

Read these instructions with your Helper.

- With your Helper, look in storage cupboards to find containers such as bottles, cans, tubs, packets, jars and bags.

- Copy down the name of each item in the containers under the correct heading on this sheet and the amount each container holds in litres (l) or millilitres (ml), kilograms (kg) or grams (g).

- Try to find at least three items for each heading.

Bottles	Cans	Tubs
Packets	**Jars**	**Bags**

Dear Helper,

This activity gives real-life experience of recognising different types of containers and looking for information on the amount each item holds. Help them to find the weight or capacity information on each item. Please do not allow your child to use items that are breakable or too heavy. Containers of strong cleaning fluids or medicines should not be handled by a child.

PHOTOCOPIABLE

Name:

Pouring drinks

You will need: a sink with a draining board, a collection of different sized empty drinks containers, some paper cups with a 'cupful' marked inside.

Read these instructions with your Helper.

- Write the names of each container as a list in the first column of the chart. Ask if you need help with spelling.

- Fill each container with water and stand them on the draining board.

- You and your Helper look at each container and write down your estimates of how many cups can be filled from the containers (you write your estimates first).

- Pour water from each container in turn into cups up to the mark until the container is empty.

- Count the number of filled cups and any half-filled cups and write the results on the chart. Empty the cups into the sink after each turn.

Name of container	Estimated number of cups		Actual number of cups
	You	Helper	

Dear Helper,

This activity is to give your child real-life experience of estimating the number of cups that can be filled from drink containers, then checking the results by carrying out the task. If your child is unfamiliar with using the notation for ½, use '3 and a bit' rather than 3½. Ask: *Were the estimates more or less than the result? Who made the closest estimates to the actual results? Which container filled the fewest/most cups?*

Name:

Hunt for squares and cubes

You will need: a pencil and a book or clipboard to rest this sheet on.

Read these instructions with your Helper.

- Search around your inside or outside your home for objects that are shaped like squares or cubes.

- Draw and write the name of each object you find on the chart. Ask if you need help with spelling the names of objects.

Squares	Cubes

Dear Helper,

This activity helps your child to recognise squares and cubes that can be found in shapes of familiar objects at home. Allow them to start looking for shapes alone then tour the home with your child to let them to show you the objects they have found. Draw your child's attention to objects they have not noticed, for example: *Can you find a square on the bathroom wall? Can you find a cube in the box of games?*

PHOTOCOPIABLE

Draw a symmetrical pattern

You will need: crayons or felt-tipped pens.

Read these instructions with your Helper.

- Colour different squares on the first half of the grid.

- Colour squares on the second half of the grid so that the pattern mirrors the pattern on the first half.

Dear Helper,

This activity lets your child practise drawing a symmetrical pattern. If your child needs help in completing the second half of the grid, guide them to count the squares between the centre line and a coloured square in the first half. They should then count the same number of squares from the centre line on the second half and colour the next square. Challenge your child by drawing another 10 × 10 square grid on the back of the sheet. Draw in a diagonal line for them to repeat the activity.

Name:

Scoop and count

Ask other members of your family to take part in this activity.

You will need: a large bowl, a large set of small countable objects and a tea tray.

Read these instructions with your Helper.

- Place the objects in the bowl. Write your name on the chart followed by your estimate of the number of objects you think you can scoop from the bowl using two hands together.

- Ask everyone taking part to do the same.

- Everyone takes a turn to scoop objects from the bowl and put them on the tray, then to group the objects into piles of ten and ones left over. Group any ones left over into fives, twos or ones as appropriate.

- You act as the scorer. Count each total by counting the '10s pile' in tens then counting on the groups of any remaining objects. Write each score on the chart.

Scooping objects

Name	Estimated number	Actual number

Dear Helper,

Encourage your child to touch each pile of ten as they count, then count on any remaining objects as groups of five, two or one. For 67 say: *10, 20,... 60 and 5 is 65 and 2 is 67*. If your child has difficulty with this, offer guidance with counting the tens piles and let your child count on any remaining objects in ones. Challenge your child to find the difference between each estimated number and the actual number by counting on in tens and/or ones from the smallest to the largest number.

Name:

Counting on and back 3

You will need: 0–99 number square, a small cube and a pencil.

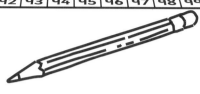

Read these instructions with your Helper.

- Throw the cube on to the square.

- Write the number it lands on in the first centre box. Count back 3 and write the number in the left-hand circle. Count on 3 and write the number in the right hand circle.

For example: (43) ←— [46] —→ (49)

Repeat to complete the sheet.

Dear Helper,

This activity is to let your child practise counting on and back 3 mentally from any number between 0 and 99. If your child has difficulty with working with numbers above 30, write different numbers between 10 and 30 in the middle boxes for them to count from. Encourage them to find the numbers on the number square then count on and back 3 in ones from each number. Challenge your child further by repeating the activity on the back of the sheet with the rule 'Count on and back 4'.

Name:

Counting in tens targets

You will need: a shuffled pile of 1–10 number cards.

Read these instructions with your Helper.

- Ask your Helper to deal you a card and set a target.
  For example, for number 4 on a card, set a target of 64.

- You write your workings on the chart, for example:

Number on card	Target number	Counting in tens
4	64	4 → 14 → 24 → 34 → 44 → 54 → 64

- Repeat to complete the sheet.

Number on card	Target number	Counting in tens

Dear Helper,

This activity lets your child practise counting in tens from any small number. To help your child with this activity use sets of 1p and 10p coins and draw this chart on another sheet: [tens | ones]
Ask them to place 1p coins on the ones column to match the number on
the card. Then to place 10p coins, one at a time, in the tens column. Say, for four 1p coins: *10 and 4 is 14; Two tens and 4 is 24* and so on. Challenge your child to count back in tens by saying a 'nineties number' instead of using cards and setting an appropriate target number. For example, 97 with the target as 27.

Name:

100 game

You will need: two sets of number cards, numbered in tens 0–100, shuffled together in a pile.

Read these instructions with your Helper.

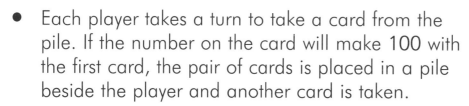

- The aim of the game is to collect pairs of cards that together make 100. At the end of the game the player with the most pairs wins.

- Start the game by each player taking one card from the pile.

- Each player takes a turn to take a card from the pile. If the number on the card will make 100 with the first card, the pair of cards is placed in a pile beside the player and another card is taken.

- If the number on the card is not needed, it is placed face up on a discard pile.

- When there are no more cards in the pile, turn over the discard pile and continue playing until there are no cards left.

Dear Helper,

This game is to help your child learn by heart all the pairs of multiples of ten that total 100. Ask them to hold up ten fingers, then put down fingers for the number on the first card. For example, for 60 (six fingers down, four up), count remaining fingers in tens saying: *10, 20, 30, 40*. Play a harder game where all the cards are spread out face down on a table. Each player turns over two cards. If the pair totals 100, the player keeps the cards and takes another turn. If the pair does not total 100, the cards are replaced face down and play passes to the other player.

Name:

Positioning numbers

You will need: a pencil.

Read these instructions with your Helper.

- Ask your Helper to say 20 different numbers between 0 and 99 one at a time.

- You work out where each number should be on a 0–99 number square and write the number in the correct place each time.

0									
									99

Dear Helper,

Encourage your child by counting down the first column in tens to the 'tens' number. For 52 this would be 50. Now count along the fifties row in ones until the correct square is reached. An easier version: write all the numbers into the 0–99 square for your child. Ask them to find and colour each number you say. Challenge your child by repeating the activity. Draw a copy of the square on the back of the sheet with 99 in the first square and 0 in the last square.

Name:

Quick change

You will need: a set of 1–30 number cards shuffled in a pile.

Read these instructions with your Helper.

- Ask your Helper to deal you three cards from the pile in a line facing you. You work out and say the total of the three numbers.

- If you are correct, your Helper places another card on top of the first card in the line for you to work out and say the total again.

- If correct, your Helper places another card on top of the second card in the line, then a card on the third card in the line and so on until all the cards have been used.

Dear Helper,

This game helps your child practise adding three numbers mentally. Remind them to find the total by starting with the highest number and counting on the other numbers in tens and/or ones. Start the game slowly at first then quicken the pace when the game is repeated. To make the game easier, lay down two cards each time instead of three. Play the game against the clock. Challenge your child to complete the game in less than 5 minutes and then in less than 2 minutes.

Name:

Add and subtract 9

You will need: a small cube and a 0–99 number square.

0	1	2	3	4	5	6	7	8	9
10	11	12	13	14	15	16	17	18	19
20	21	22	23	24	25	26	27	28	29
30		32	33	34	35	36	37	38	39
40		42	43	44	45	46	47	48	49
50	51	52	53	54	55	56	57	58	59
60	61	62	63	64	65	66	67	68	69
70	71	72	73	74	75	76	77	78	79
80	81	82	83	84	85	86	87	88	89
90	91	92	93	94	95	96	97	98	99

Read these instructions with your Helper.

- Throw the cube on the square, write down the number it lands on, then the 'add 9' number. For 36, for example, write 36 → 45.

- Ask your Helper to time the game. How many 'add nines' can you complete in one minute?

- Play the game again with the rule 'Subtract 9'.

I completed ⬜ 'add nines'.   I completed ⬜ 'subtract nines'.

Dear Helper,

This game is to help your child to practise adding and subtracting 9 mentally starting from any number up to 99. Encourage them to add and subtract 9 by adding 10 then adjusting by 1. Repeat the games to see if your child can beat their first scores. Challenge your child to repeat the games with the rules 'Add 19' and 'Subtract 19'.

SOLVING PROBLEMS

NUMBER PROBLEMS IN MONEY

Name:

£5.00 problem

Gran keeps loose change in a tin.
She needs to pay the milkman £5.00

- Colour the coins Gran could use to pay the milk bill.

- Complete the chart and count the total money in Gran's tin.

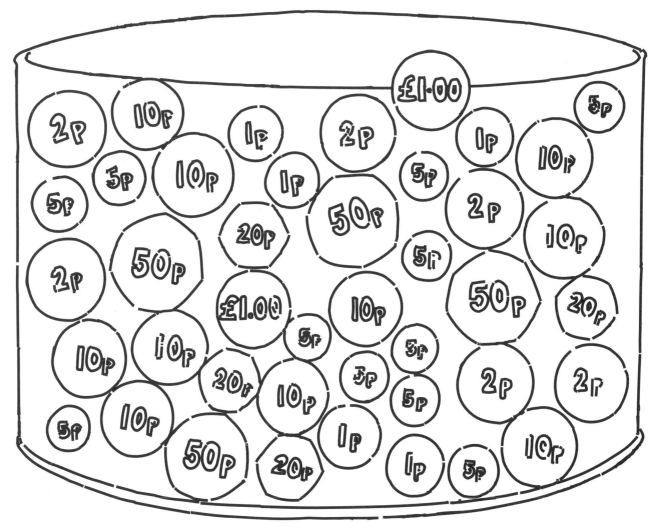

Coins	£1.00	50p	20p	10p	5p	2p	1p	Total money in Gran's tin
Total money								

Dear Helper,

This activity gives your child a real-life experience of sorting and counting coins to make up an amount. If your child needs help, encourage them to match each coin picture with a real coin, then sort the coins into piles for counting. Challenge your child to work out how much more money Gran would need in her tin to pay a paper bill of £7.00 instead of the milk bill.

Quick multiplication games

You will need: one suit of shuffled playing cards, Ace to 10.

Read these instructions with your Helper.

Multiply by 2

- Recite the 2 times table to your Helper.

- Ask your Helper to hold up one card at a time. You multiply the number on the card by 2 (using Ace as 1). If you are correct, your Helper gives you the card.

- Continue until you have all the cards.

Multiply by 10

- Play the game in the same way as 'Multiply by 2', but with 10.

Dear Helper,

These games are to help your child to learn by heart all the multiplication facts for the 2 and 10 times tables. Play the games slowly at first then quicken the pace. If your child has difficulty multiplying a number by 2 or 10, ask them to count on in twos or tens as you point to each spot on the card. Challenge your child by using 'multiply by 2 and 10' in the same game. You hold up a card and say the rule for each card, 'multiply by 2' or 'multiply by 10'. Try playing the game with the rule 'multiply by 5'.

Name:

Double a double

You will need: a box of dominoes.

Read these instructions with your Helper.

- Spread out the dominoes face down on a table.

- Pick up one domino and draw a picture of the domino on the sheet.

- Double the number of spots on the domino, then double that number again. For example:

For  write $4 + 4 = 8$

$8 + 8 = 16$

- How many can you complete in 5 minutes?

Dear Helper,

This activity is to help your child to practise doubling numbers mentally, writing the answers as sums. Make the activity easier by asking them to double the number once each time. They could count the spots on each domino twice if help is required. Challenge your child to double the number three times.
For example: $4 + 4 = 8$ $8 + 8 = 16$ $16 + 16 = 32$

Name:

Shop for sweets

You will need: a spotted dice, a shaker and a copy of this sheet for each player.

Read the rules of the game with your Helper.

- Each player takes a turn to throw the dice to see how many of each type of sweet to buy. Start with the first type of sweet on the chart. The example is for a 5 thrown on the dice. Now work out the cost.

Sweet	Price	Number to buy	Total cost
Cola Fizzers	1p	5	5p

- At the end of the game each player works out the total number of sweets bought, money spent and the total change from £2.00.

Sweet	Price	Number to buy	Total cost
Cola Fizzers	1p		
Mint balls	2p		
Lollipops	3p		
Nut bars	4p		
Candy sticks	5p		
Lucky dip	10p		
	Totals		
		Change from £2.00	

Dear Helper,

This activity helps your child to work out the cost of buying multiple items, to find the total cost and then work out the change from £2.00. If help is required, let your child use coins to work out the costs and the change from £2.00. At the end, compare results with your child. *Who bought the most/fewest sweets? Who spent the most/least money?*
Make the activity more challenging by playing with two dice, finding the total spent and change from £5.00.

Quick double and half games

You will need: a shuffled set of 2–20 even numbered cards.

Read these instructions with your Helper.

Double the number

- Ask your Helper to hold up one card at a time. You double the number. If you are correct, your Helper gives you the card. Continue until you have all the cards.

Halve the number

- Play the game in the same way as 'Double the number', but halving each number.

Dear Helper,

These games will help your child learn by heart the double and half numbers of all even numbers to 20. Play the games slowly at first, then quicken the pace. If help is required, let your child use small countable objects to make up the number. Challenge your child by using the double and half rules in the same game. You hold up a card and say the rule for each card, double the number or halve the number. Give your child a counter for every correct answer.

Name:

Measure up

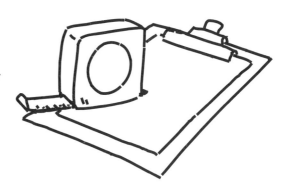

You will need: your worksheet, a pencil, a 1m length of string or a tape measure and a clipboard or book to rest the sheet on.

Read these instructions with your Helper.

- Ask your Helper to work with you to estimate and measure some long lengths to the nearest metre around your house and garden, using a tape measure or string.

- Write the results on the chart. Ask if you need help with spelling the names of the items.

- You write your estimate before your Helper each time.

Item measured	Estimates		Actual length to the nearest metre
	You	Your Helper	
_____	_____	_____	_____
_____	_____	_____	_____
_____	_____	_____	_____
_____	_____	_____	_____
_____	_____	_____	_____
_____	_____	_____	_____
_____	_____	_____	_____
_____	_____	_____	_____
_____	_____	_____	_____

Dear Helper,

This activity is to give your child a real-life experience of estimating and measuring long lengths to the nearest metre. Show your child how to use 1m length of string or a tape measure safely. Let your child read the measurements on the tape each time, offering guidance where appropriate. For example, help your child to find the nearest 100cm mark. Challenge your child to make estimates and measurements in metres and centimetres to the nearest centimetre, for example 6m 34cm.

Domino divides

You will need: a box of dominoes.

Read these instructions with your Helper.

- Sort out the dominoes with an even number of spots. Discard odd numbered dominoes and the double blank.

- Spread out the even numbered dominoes face down on a table.

- Pick up a domino and draw a picture of the domino on the sheet.

- Divide the number of spots by 2.

  For  write $6 \div 2 = 3$

- How many can you complete in 2 minutes?

I have completed [ ] domino divides.

Dear Helper,

This activity is to help your child to practise dividing small numbers by 2 without a remainder. If help is required, tell your child to make each domino number with small countable objects, then split the objects into groups of two and count the number of groups. Challenge your child to pick up two dominoes each time, find the total number of spots and then divide the total by 2. Try using all the dominoes, including odds and include ones left over as remainders. For 5 write $5 \div 2 = 2$ r 1.

Food trail

You will need: a notebook and pencil.

Read these instructions with your Helper.

- Ask your Helper to help you to find ten food items packed in bags or packets. If possible you could do this with your Helper at the supermarket.

- Find out from the labels how much each item weighs in kilograms or grams and write your results in the notebook.

- Back at home, copy your results onto the chart on this sheet. Draw a ring round the heaviest item and the lightest item.

Name of item	Weight in kg or g

Dear Helper,

This activity is to give your child a real-life experience of looking at food packaging labels to find out how much each item weighs in kilograms or grams. Use food labels from your own home if you cannot get to the supermarket. To save time at the supermarket, you could print the name of each item for the child in the notebook. Challenge your child when you are back at home to order the items from heaviest to lightest in the notebook before copying the results in order on to the sheet.

SOLVING PROBLEMS

ORGANISING AND USING DATA

Sweet sort

You will need: a bag of assorted sweets.

Read these instructions with your Helper.

- Sort the sweets into types, by colour or shape.

- Write names for each type of sweet on the chart. Ask if you need help with the spelling.

- Count and colour one square on the chart for each sweet.

Number of sweets

Type of sweet	1	2	3	4	5	6	7	8	9	10	11	12

Dear Helper,

When the graph is complete, discuss the results with your child. Ask: *Which type of sweet has the highest/lowest number? Do any types of sweets have the same number? How many sweets were there altogether?* To make the task easier, write the names of each type of sweet on the chart for your child. Let your child count the sweets and write the number beside each name before colouring the squares on the chart. Challenge your child to find totals of two types of sweets and the difference in numbers between two types of sweets.

Name:

Telling the time

| o'clock | half-past | quarter-past | quarter-to |

Write the time underneath each clock.
Work across each row.

Dear Helper,

This activity gives your child practice in telling and writing times to the hour, half-hour and quarter-hours. If your child has difficulty working with the assorted times, first point to each o'clock time for your child to complete, then each half-past time and so on. If your child completes the sheet correctly without help, draw the following chart on another sheet. Challenge them to write down the time on each clock then the time one hour later.

Time given	One hour later
half-past 8	half-past 9

Two-way counts

You will need: 0–99 number square, a small cube and a pencil.

Read these instructions with your Helper.

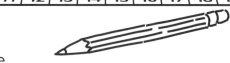

- Throw the cube onto the grid.

- Write the number it lands on into the first centre box.

- Count back 4 and write the number in the left-hand circle.

- Count on 4 and write the number in the right-hand circle.

- Repeat to complete the first column.

- Use the rule 'count back 5 / count on 5' to complete the second column.

example

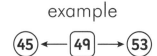

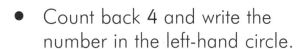

| Count back 4 / count on 4 | Count back 5 / count on 5 |

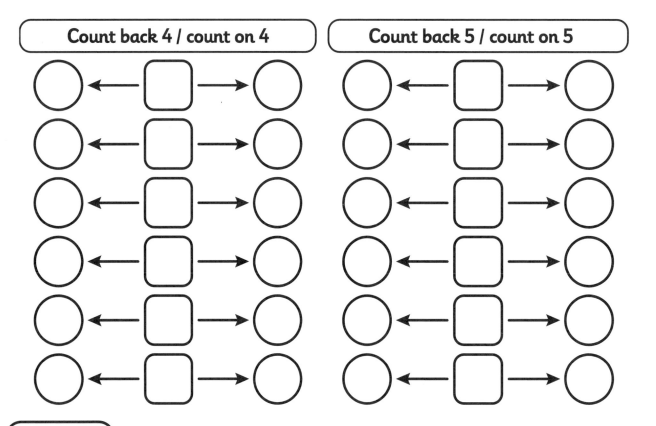

Dear Helper,

This activity is to help your child to practise counting on and back 4 and 5 from any number between 0 and 99. If your child has difficulty working with numbers above 30, write different numbers between 10 and 25 in the middle boxes instead of using the 0–99 grid and cube. Let them use the 0–99 grid to help with counting. Challenge your child further by repeating the activity on the back of the sheet with the rule 'count back / count on 6'.

Name:

Counting on game

You will need: a shuffled suit of playing cards, Ace to 10 (e.g. diamonds), a cube/dice marked with numbers 1, 2, 3, 4, 5 and 10.

Read these instructions with your Helper.

- Ask your Helper to deal you a card.

- You roll the dice to decide the 'counting on' rule. For example, a 2 rolled means 'count on in twos'.

- Count aloud from the number on the card using the counting rule to the tenth number in the sequence, or as far you can.

- Point to each of the ten stars as you count to help you know when to stop.

- Play the game until you have been dealt all the cards.

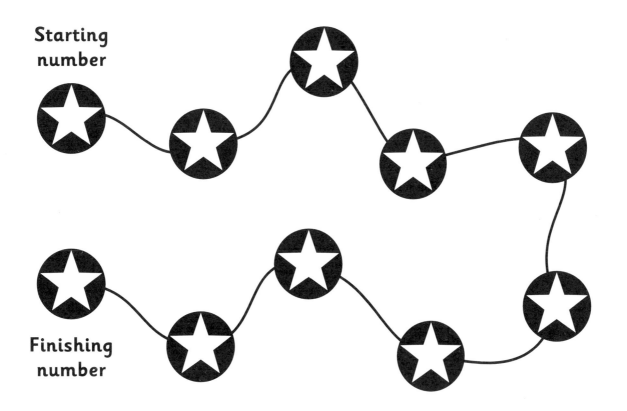

Starting number

Finishing number

Dear Helper,

This game is to help your child to count on mentally from any small number in steps of either 1, 2, 3, 4, 5 or 10. If your child needs help with this, ask your child to write out each number sequence as far as possible on another sheet, using fingers to help them count from one number to the next. Challenge your child to continue each counting sequence to a 'nineties' number or to 100 where appropriate.

PHOTOCOPIABLE

CALCULATIONS

MENTAL CALCULATIONS + AND –

Adding three numbers

You will need: a shuffled pack of playing cards, Ace to 10.

Read these instructions with your Helper.

- Ask your Helper to deal you three cards placed face up on a table.

- You find the total by starting with the largest number or finding a pair totalling 10.

- If your answer is correct, you keep the cards and your Helper deals you three more.

- Continue until all the cards have been dealt.

Dear Helper,

This game is to help your child add three small numbers mentally. Play the game slowly at first, then quicken the pace. If your child gets stuck, tell them to rearrange the cards so the largest number is first or to find a pair of cards totalling 10. If more help is required, encourage your child to use the symbols on the cards to help with counting on from the largest number or to form a pair totalling 10. Challenge your child further by dealing four cards each time.

Find the difference

You will need: two shuffled suits of playing cards, Ace to 10 (e.g. diamonds and spades), a margarine tub.

Read these instructions with your Helper.

- Place the two suits of playing cards in two piles face down on a table.

- Take one card from each pile and write the numbers on the sheet as a difference statement and find the answer, for example:

- Place the cards in the tub and take two more cards.

- Repeat until all cards have been used.

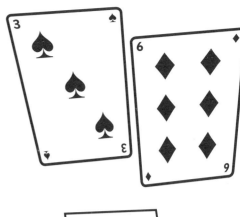

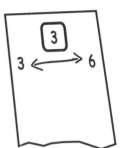

Dear Helper,

This activity is to help your child to find the difference between two numbers mentally. If your child needs help, tell them to count on from the smaller number to the larger number using fingers or the symbols on a card. Shuffle each pile of cards and repeat the activity to challenge your child further.

Name:

Four in a row

A game for two players.

You will need: 0–99 number square, a large set of coloured counters for each player (e.g. red and blue), a shuffled pack of playing cards, Ace to 9.

Read these instructions with your Helper.

- Place the pack of cards face down on a table. Each player sits facing the 0–99 grid with their coloured counters.

- Each player takes a turn to pick up two cards and place them face up on the table to make a two-digit number (tens and units).

Different numbers can be made by changing the order of the cards or by subtracting the units number from the chosen tens number:

for ♥ (2) and ♥♥♥♥ (4) this could be 24 (20 + 4) or 42 (40 + 2) or 16 (20 − 4) or 38 (40 − 2)

- Each player says the number they have chosen to make, then places a counter on that number on the 0–99 number square.

- When all cards have been used, re-shuffle the cards to continue.

- The first player to get four counters in a row is the winner, for example:

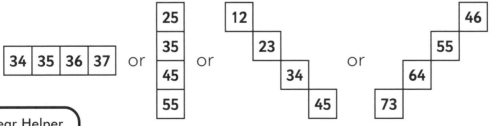

| 34 | 35 | 36 | 37 |

or

25
35
45
55

or

12
23
34
45

or

46
55
64
73

Dear Helper,

Add/subtract 19 and 21 games

You will need: a shuffled set of playing cards 2s–8s and a 0–99 number square.

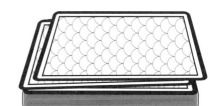

Read these instructions with your Helper.

- Ask your Helper to deal you two cards in a line facing you. Count the first card as a tens number and the second card as a units number.

- Find the number on the 0–99 number square and add 19 to the number, for example:

for the cards [4♦] and [6♠] find 46 on the square, then add 19 to the number (add 20, subtract 1), saying the answer: '65'.

- If you are correct, you keep the cards.

- Continue playing until all cards have been used.

- Shuffle the cards and repeat the game with the rules 'subtract 19', then 'add 21' and 'subtract 21'.

Dear Helper,

These games help your child to mentally add or subtract 19 and 21 from a given two-digit number. Make the games easier by sorting the cards into two piles of red and black suits. Tell your child that the red cards are 'tens' numbers and black cards are 'units' numbers. Deal them one card from each pile. Guide your child to count the spots on the red card in tens, then to count on the black card spots in ones to establish the number each time. Challenge them to carry out the additions and subtractions mentally without using the 0–99 number square.

Name:

Difference patterns

You will need: 0–99 number square.

Read these instructions with your Helper.

0	1	2	3	4	5	6	7	8	9
10	11	12	13	14	15	16	17	18	19
20	21	22	23	24	25	26	27	28	29
30	31	32	33	34	35	36	37	38	39
40	41	42	43	44	45	46	47	48	49
50	51	52	53	54	55	56	57	58	59
60	61	62	63	64	65	66	67	68	69
70	71	72	73	74	75	76	77	78	79
80	81	82	83	84	85	86	87	88	89
90	91	92	93	94	95	96	97	98	99

- Use the number square to find ten pairs of numbers with a difference of 9 and write your answers in the correct column below.

  For example: **26 ⟷ 35**

- Repeat the activity with ten pairs of numbers with a difference of 19. Do the same with ten pairs of numbers with a difference of 11, then 21.

Difference of 9	Difference of 19	Difference of 11	Difference of 21

Dear Helper,

This activity is to help your child to recognise that pairs of numbers with the same difference form a number pattern on a 0–99 grid. This will help them to develop better mental arithmetic skills. To make the activity easier, tell your child to complete differences of 9 and 11 before attempting differences of 19 and 21. Challenge your child to see how many of each difference they can complete in one minute.

Name:

Trios

Read these instructions with your Helper.

13	24	28	17	21
26	29	30	12	23
11	20	16	25	18
19	15	22	17	14

- Choose three different numbers from the grid and write each number in a box on the first diagram, for example: for 12, 24 and 28:

- Find the total in your head by adding the 'tens' numbers first, then counting on the 'ones' in the easiest order to find the total, for example: *20 and 20 and 10 is 50, 50 and 8 is 58, and 2 is 60, and 4 is 64.*

- Write the total in the centre of the diagram.

- Repeat to complete the sheet.

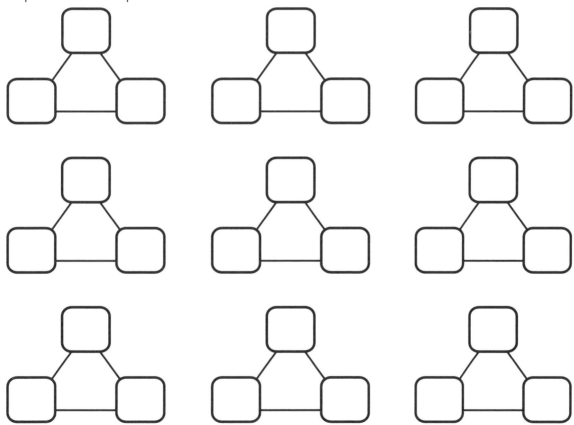

Dear Helper,

This activity helps your child to find the total of three two-digit numbers mentally. If your child finds this difficult, encourage them to write workings underneath each diagram, for example: 20 + 20 + 10 = 50, 8 + 2 + 4 = 10 + 4 = 14, 50 + 14 = 64. Extend by asking your child to repeat the activity on another sheet, drawing a trio diagram to record each solution.

Subtracting 'teens' numbers

23	30	25	29	36
37	22	27	20	38
24	35	39	34	21
32	26	31	28	33

16	11	15
12	17	14
18	13	19

Read these instructions with your Helper.

- Choose one number from each grid to write a subtraction statement.

- Subtract the 'teens' number by counting back 10 from the first number, then subtracting the 'ones', for example:

  For 29 – 14, write 29 – 10 = 19, 19 – 4 = 15.

- Write a statement using each number in the second grid at least once.

Dear Helper,

This activity helps your child to develop the mental skill of subtracting numbers above ten from two-digit numbers. Let your child use small countable objects if help is required. Challenge your child to work the answers out mentally without writing workings where possible, writing, for example, 29 – 14 = 15.

Name:

Shopping with £5.00

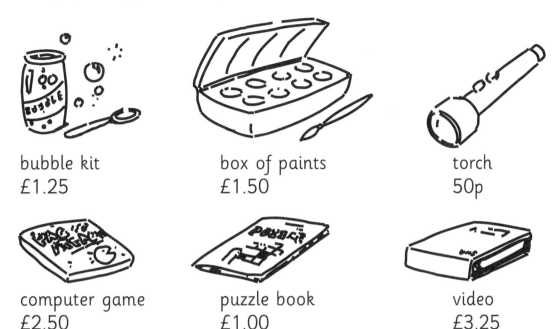

bubble kit
£1.25

box of paints
£1.50

torch
50p

computer game
£2.50

puzzle book
£1.00

video
£3.25

Find four different ways to buy two items with £5.00.

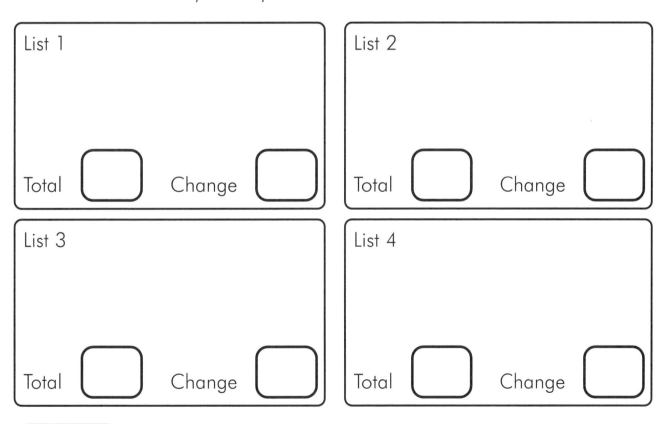

List 1

Total [　]   Change [　]

List 2

Total [　]   Change [　]

List 3

Total [　]   Change [　]

List 4

Total [　]   Change [　]

Dear Helper,

This shopping activity is to help your child to practise addition of money to find the total cost and the change from £5.00 If your child gets stuck, encourage them to make each amount in the least number of coins, then find the total by grouping coins of the same type together and counting the groups starting with the coins of the largest value. Help your child to find the change the 'shopkeeper's way' (using coins to count on from the total to £5.00). Challenge your child to shop with £10.00 instead of £5.00, choosing three or more items to buy each time.

PHOTOCOPIABLE

Name:

Treasure hunt

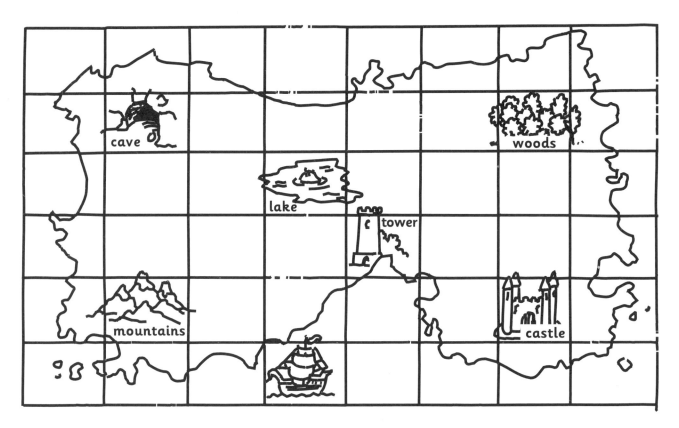

Follow these directions and count the squares.

↑	↓	←	→
up	down	left	right

Start at the ship.

1   2   3   4   5

6   7   8   9   10

The treasure is buried _____ .

Dear Helper,

This activity is to help your child to find a route by following directions. Help your child count the squares if required. Challenge them to find a different place to hide the treasure and then write a set of secret directions to find it from the ship.

PHOTOCOPIABLE

Knock down nine-pins

A game for two players.

You will need: squared paper and a pencil for each player.

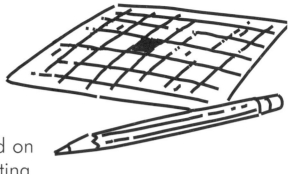

Read these instructions with your Helper.

- Each player draws a 9 × 9 square grid on squared paper, colours the centre starting square, and draws a record chart.

- Each player secretly draws in nine pins on nine different squares, for example:

- Each player takes a turn to find the position of the pins on their opponent's sheet by giving directions in two moves from the starting square such as: 'Up three squares, left two squares'.

- If there is a pin marked in that square the player has scored a hit. The opponent marks the square with a cross to show that the pin has been knocked down ⊠.

- Each player keeps a record of the directions given each time and notes the result in a chart (see example opposite). If the directions land them on a square next to a pin the opponent should say: 'Near miss.'

- The first player to knock down all nine pins is the winner.

Record chart		
1st move	2nd move	Result
↑3 ↓2 ↑1	←2 →3 ←4	Hit Near miss Miss

Dear Helper,

This game is to help your child to develop the skill of giving simple directions for moving along a route using 'up', 'down', 'left' and 'right'. If they find difficulty remembering the positions of the opponent's squares that have been targeted, let your child colour squares on their own grid to show hits, misses and near misses. Give guidance where appropriate. An easier version, use a 5 × 5 square grid and mark in five pins. Extend by repeating the game, placing the nine pins in different squares.

Name:

Making carrot and orange soup

You will need: a food processor or hand blender, a wooden spoon, a measuring jug and a saucepan.

Read these instructions with your Helper. Then work together.

Ingredients for 4 people.

540g can of carrots
1 chicken stock cube
$\frac{3}{4}$ pint (600ml) hot water
$\frac{1}{4}$ pint (200ml) orange juice
Pepper

Preparation and cooking time about 10 minutes.

- Puree the carrots using a processor or blender and put in saucepan.

- Dissolve the stock cube in $\frac{3}{4}$ pint (600ml) of hot water in the measuring jug.

- Add the stock and the orange juice to the saucepan and stir well. Add pepper to taste.

- Simmer gently for 5 minutes and serve hot with crusty bread.

Dear Helper,

This activity is to help your child to use units of mass/weight and capacity in a real life situation to make some soup. Challenge your child further by carrying out other cooking or food preparation sessions. Choose further recipes to share from a simple cookery book such as Jane Suthering's *Children's Quick and Easy Cookbook* (published in the UK by Dorling Kindersley). IMPORTANT NOTE: As the kitchen is a potentially dangerous environment (hot liquids, electrical appliances and sharp objects), make sure that you supervise your child throughout this activity.

Name:

Symmetrical shapes and patterns

You will need: a pencil, crayons or felt-tipped pens and a book or clip board to rest the sheet on.

Read these instructions with your Helper.

- Search around your home for items that are symmetrical or show a symmetrical pattern.

- Draw, colour and write the name of each item you find on the chart marking in the line of symmetry each time.

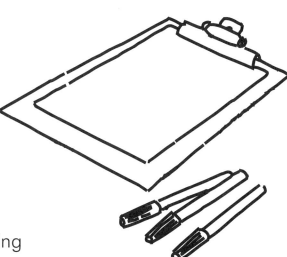

Symmetrical shapes and patterns

Dear Helper,

This activity is to help your child to recognise symmetry in everyday objects. For an item to be symmetrical, both halves have to be the same shape or show the same pattern like the reflection in a mirror. Allow your child to start looking for items alone, then tour the home allowing them to show you the items they have found. Draw your child's attention to items they have not noticed, for example: *Is the lamp in the sitting room symmetrical? Is the chest of drawers symmetrical?*

Count back, count on

You will need: 0–99 number square, a small cube, a cube/dice marked with numbers 1, 2, 3, 4, 5 and 10.

0	1	2	3	4	5	6	7	8	9
10	11	12	13	14	15	16	17	18	19
20	21	22	23	24	25	26	27	28	29
30	31	32	33	34	35	36	37	38	39
40	41	42	43	44	45	46	47	48	49
50	51	52	53	54	55	56	57	58	59
60	61	62	63	64	65	66	67	68	69
70	71	72	73	74	75	76	77	78	79
80	81	82	83	84	85	86	87	88	89
90	91	92	93	94	95	96	97	98	99

Read these instructions with your Helper.

- Throw the cube on the square. Write down the number it lands on in the first centre box, for example: ○ ← 36 → ○

- Roll the dice to find the counting rule, for example '3'. Write down the number over each arrow, for example:
  ○ ←3— 36 —3→ ○

- Count back 3 from the number in the box and write the answer in the left-hand circle.

- Count on 3 from the number in the box and write the answer in the right-hand circle.

- Continue throwing the cube and rolling the dice to complete 10 two-way counting statements.

(count back) (count on)

(33) ←3— [36] —3→ (39)

( ) ← [ ] → ( )

( ) ← [ ] → ( )

( ) ← [ ] → ( )

( ) ← [ ] → ( )

( ) ← [ ] → ( )

( ) ← [ ] → ( )

( ) ← [ ] → ( )

( ) ← [ ] → ( )

( ) ← [ ] → ( )

( ) ← [ ] → ( )

Dear Helper,

This activity is to help your child to practise counting on and counting back mentally from any given number using counting rules that have been learned in school. Give guidance where appropriate and encourage your child to use the 0–99 number square if help is required. Challenge your child further by carrying out the activity against the clock.

Name:

Double it, halve it

You will need: a shuffled set of number cards marked in multiples of 5 (5–50) and a shuffled set of number cards marked in multiples of 10 (10–100).

Read these instructions with your Helper.

Double the number

- Use cards 5–50. Ask your Helper to hold up one card at a time. You double the number. If you are correct, your Helper gives you the card. Continue until you have all the cards.

Halve the number

- Use cards 10–100. Play the game in the same way as 'Double the number', but this time halve the number.

Dear Helper,

These games help your child learn by heart the doubles of all numbers in the 5 times table and the halves of all numbers in the 10 times table. Play the games slowly at first, then quicken the pace. If help is required, let your child use a collection of 10p and 5p coins to make up each number. Then count the total in one group. Challenge your child by using both sets of cards in a 'Double or halve?' game. If the number ends in a 5 the number is doubled. If the number ends in a zero, the number is halved.

Name:

Counting back game

You will need: a shuffled set of 91–100 number cards, a cube/dice marked with numbers 1, 2, 3, 4, 5 and 10, a 0–99 number square if help is required.

0	1	2	3	4	5	6	7	8	9
10	11	12	13	14	15	16	17	18	19
20	21	22	23	24	25	26	27	28	29
30	31	32	33	34	35	36	37	38	39
40	41	42	43	44	45	46	47	48	49
50	51	52	53	54	55	56	57	58	59
60	61	62	63	64	65	66	67	68	69
70	71	72	73	74	75	76	77	78	79
80	81	82	83	84	85	86	87	88	89
90	91	92	93	94	95	96	97	98	99

Read these instructions with your Helper.

- Ask your Helper to deal you a card.

- You roll the dice to decide the 'counting back' rule. For example, a 5 rolled means 'count back in fives'.

- Count back aloud from the number on the card using the counting rule to the tenth number in the sequence, or as far as possible.

- Point to each of the ten stars as you count to help you know when to stop.

- Play the game until you have been dealt all the cards.

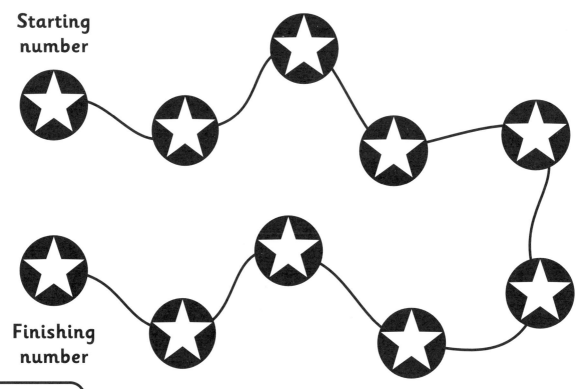

Starting number

Finishing number

Dear Helper,

This game is to help your child to mentally count back from any 'nineties' number in steps of 1, 2, 3, 4, 5 or 10. If your child needs help with this, encourage them to use the 0–99 number square to help with the counting and to write out each number sequence to the tenth number or as far as possible on another sheet. Challenge your child to continue each counting sequence down to a number between 1 and 9 or 0 where appropriate.

Name:

Hundreds and thousands

A game for two or more players.

You will need: two sets of cards numbered in tens 10–90, two sets of cards numbered in hundreds 100–900, a pile of counters and a score sheet.

Ask other members of your family to play this game with you.

Rules of the game

- Shuffle the sets of cards together. The first player deals out eight cards on a table in two lines of four.

- If a pair of cards adds to 100 or 1000 the player may cover each card with another card (see below). The first player continues covering pairs of cards until no more pairs are found.

- Count the remaining cards in the pack and write down the number on a score sheet.

- Each player takes a turn at the game.

- At the end of the round, the player with the lowest score wins a counter. If there is a tie, both take a counter.

- Play the game for as long as you like. At the end, the player with the most counters wins.

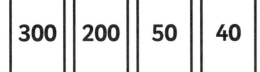

| 100 | 50 | 200 | 700 |

| 300 | 200 | 50 | 40 |

Here the two '50' cards making 100 can be covered with two more cards. The '700' and '300' cards making 1000 can also be covered.

Round	John	Sue	Mum
1	3		
2			
3			

Dear Helper,

This game is to help your child to learn by heart pairs of 'tens' numbers that make 100 and pairs of 'hundreds' numbers that make 1000. Before the game, prepare a sheet with the names of all the players along the top and number of rounds down the side. Let your child write down the scores and decide the winner in each round. Give guidance by pointing out any pairs your child may have missed until they are familiar with the game.

PHOTOCOPIABLE

Domino subtraction

You will need: a box of dominoes, a pencil and a sheet of paper.

Read these instructions with your Helper.

- Spread the dominoes out face down on a table.

- Pick up and draw a picture of two dominoes on the sheet, mark in the spots, then write the two-digit number for each domino underneath each one.

- Write a subtraction statement by placing the largest number first and using the easiest method to carry out the subtraction, for example:

Use the method of subtracting the smaller number from the larger number.

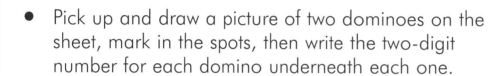

20 – 10

Use the method of counting on from the smaller number to the larger number to find the difference.

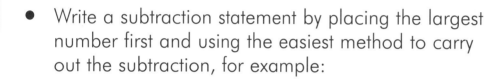

25 – 21

Use the method of starting with the larger number, subtracting the tens then the units of the smaller number.

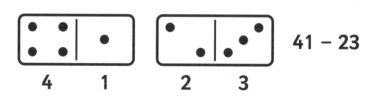

41 – 23

- Write subtraction statements for ten pairs of dominoes.

Dear Helper,

This activity helps your child to practise subtracting larger numbers and to decide which is the easiest method to use to carry out the subtraction. Encourage your child to work mentally where they can, but to write workings if they are unsure. If extra help is required, encourage them to make each number with 10p and 1p coins. Challenge your child further by asking them to check each subtraction by adding the smaller number to the answer. If the new answer is the same as the larger number, then the statement is correct.

Name:

Pay and change from £5.00

You will need: Some 1p, 2p, 5p, 10p, 20p, 50p, £1.00 and £2.00 coins.

Read these instructions with your Helper.

- Imagine you have £5.00. Choose four amounts from the circles below and write the total in the 'Pay' column.

- Work out the change from £5.00 and write the amount in the 'Change' column.

- Draw the amount of change in money using the least number of coins.

- Repeat to complete the sheet.

Pay	Change	Change in the least number of coins

Dear Helper,

This activity helps your child to add amounts of money and work out what the change will be from £5.00 in the least number of coins. Encourage your child to add the amounts in the circles by putting the largest amount first, then counting on the other amounts in order of value. They should then work out the change the 'shopkeeper's way', by counting on from the total to the next 10p, then in tens to the next £1.00 and in £1.00s to £5.00. Challenge your child by drawing another circle marked £5.00 and including a £5.00 note in the collection of cash, for your child to find change from £10.00.

Name:

Subtraction game

You will need: a set of 10–40 number cards.

Read these instructions with your Helper.

- Ask your Helper to deal you two cards face up.

- Subtract the smaller number from the larger number and say the answer. If you are correct, you keep the cards and your Helper deals you two more cards.

- Continue until all cards have been dealt.

Dear Helper,

This game is to help your child to subtract a two-digit number from a larger number mentally. Play the game slowly at first, then quicken the pace. If your child gets stuck, guide your child to use one of the following methods: for subtractions such as 27 – 24, count on from the smaller to the larger number in ones to find the difference; for subtractions such as 36 – 25, start with the larger number, subtracting the tens then the units of the smaller number. To challenge your child further, use a set of 20–50 number cards. Try using a set of 10–100 number cards.

Name:

5 times table

A game for two players.

You will need: a pencil, a paperclip and 20 counters.

Read these instructions with your Helper.

- Use the paperclip with the tip of a pencil as a spinner placed on the centre of the circle below. Work the spinner by flicking the paperclip so that it spins around the pencil point.

- Each player takes turns to spin the clip. Multiply the number the clip stops at by 5 and place a counter on the answer number on their grid.

- The first player to cover all ten numbers on the grid is the winner.

- Repeat the game a few times.

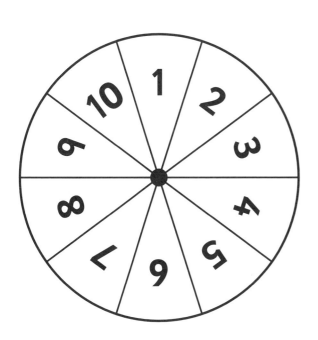

1st player

30	5	25	15	40
20	45	10	50	35

2nd player

30	5	25	15	40
20	45	10	50	35

Dear Helper,

This game is to help your child to learn by heart all the facts of the 5 times table. If your child needs help, encourage them to hold up fingers to match the number on the spinner, then touch each finger, counting in fives to find the answer. Challenge your child further after the game by asking questions such as: *What is the total of six fives? How many fives in 50?*

Name:

Double and halve

Read these instructions with your Helper.

22	34	40	36	28
50	42	24	48	32
46	30	38	44	26

- Write a number from the grid in the middle box of the first drawing.

- Double the number and write the answer in the top box.

- Halve the number and write the answer in the bottom box.

- Cross out each number on the grid as you use it.

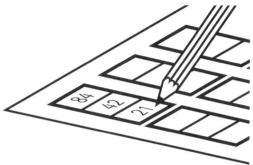

Double and halve

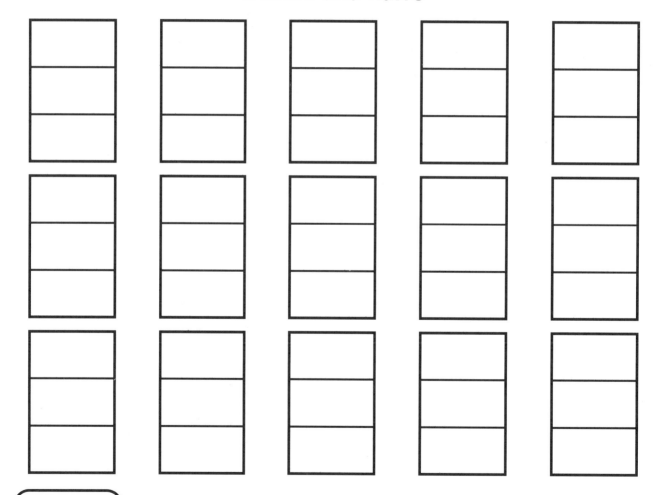

Dear Helper,

This activity is to help your child to practise doubling and halving the same number and to begin to recognise that halving is the inverse of doubling. To make the activity easier, encourage your child to use the numbers in order, starting with 22, then 24 and so on. Challenge your child further by covering up their work and saying a number from the grid and asking your child to double then halve the number each time.

PHOTOCOPIABLE

Name:

Domino multiplication

You will need: a box of dominoes.

Read these instructions with your Helper.

- Discard double 6 and double blank dominoes and spread the others out face down on a table.

- Pick up a domino and draw a picture of the domino in the first column. Write a multiplication for the spots on the domino, then write the equivalent repeated addition, for example:

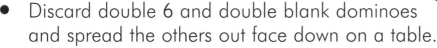	3 × 2 = 6	3 + 3 = 6

Dear Helper, • Repeat this with nine more dominoes.

This activity is to help your child to practise multiplying two numbers and then to write an equivalent sum using repeated addition. If your child needs help with a multiplication tell your child to use the first domino number as the counting number, then to touch each spot of the second number during the count, for example, for 4 × 3 (counting number is 4) so say: *4, 8, 12.* For the equivalent repeated addition, tell them to use the second domino number as the counting number (3), then to write the first number three times, for example, 4 + 4 + 4 = 12. Challenge your child to repeat the activity using the spots on two dominoes, for example: 5 × 3 = 15, 5 + 5 + 5 = 15.

Super saver

You will need: a note book and pencil.

Read these instructions with your Helper.

- Ask your Helper to plan some time to take you to a supermarket to look for ten 'saver' items.

- Use your notebook to copy down the name and the price of the item, for example, 'Saver Baked Beans 19p'. Then look on the shelf to find the most expensive item of the same type and copy down the name and the price of the item.

- Back at home copy your results to the chart on this sheet.

- Work out the amount of money that would be saved by buying a saver item instead of the most expensive one.

Name of item	Most expensive	Cheapest	Money saved

Dear Helper,

This activity is to give your child a real-life experience of comparing prices between branded and supermarket 'saver' items and to work out how much money would be saved by buying the cheaper item. To save time at the supermarket, you could print the name of each item in the note book. Challenge your child further by asking them to work out the total savings from buying two of the cheaper items.

Help your child to use a calculator to find out the total savings if one of each saver item was bought.

Name:

Multiply and divide by 2 game

You will need: a shuffled set of 1–20 number cards.

Read these instructions with your Helper.

- Ask your Helper to hold up one card each time.

- If the number is 'odd', you multiply the number by 2.

- If the number is 'even', you divide the number by 2.

- If you are correct, your Helper gives you the card.

- Continue until you have all the cards.

Dear Helper,

This game is to provide practice in multiplying and dividing numbers by 2. Play the game slowly at first then quicken the pace. An easier version: use only even numbered cards 2–20. Play the game with the rule 'multiply by 2', then repeat the game with the rule 'divide by 2'. A harder version: use cards 1–20. Play the game with the rule 'multiply by 2'. Repeat the game with the rule 'divide by 2', where your child is expected to include answers with remainders when dividing the odd numbers, for example: 13 ÷ 2 = 6 r1.

MENTAL CALCULATIONS × AND ÷   CALCULATIONS

Name:

Four in a line

Multiplication game for two players.

You will need: a shuffled pack of playing cards Ace to 10, a cube marked 2, 2, 5, 5, 10, 10, a shaker, a pile of coloured counters, one colour for each player (e.g. red and blue) and a margarine tub.

Rules of the game

- Place the pack of playing cards face down on a table with the tub. Give each player a pile of counters.

- Each player takes a turn to pick up a card and roll the dice. The player multiplies the number on the card by the number on the dice, finds the answer number on the grid and covers it with a counter. The card is then placed in the tub.

- If all squares showing the answer number are covered with counters, play passes to the other player.

- First player with four counters in a line is the winner, for example:

5	16	8	20	14	35	15
45	10	2	18	5	70	35
25	6	15	2	60	45	4
18	20	80	40	6	12	20
15	30	4	10	50	20	5
90	6	10	30	8	50	12
5	14	40	25	100	16	10

Dear Helper,

This game is to help your child practise multiplying numbers by 2, 10 and 5 and to become familiar with the facts of the 2, 10 and 5 times tables. If your child gets stuck, encourage them to touch each spot on a card and count using the number on the dice, for example, for the card ⦂⦂ and a dice showing ②, say: 2, 4, 6, 8. To make the game more challenging, introduce blocking tactics by placing a counter on a number to stop the other player making a line.

Name:

Shop for fruit

A game for two or more players.

You will need: a copy of this sheet for each player, a spotted dice and a shaker.

Ask other members of your family to play this game with you.

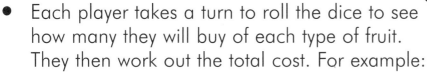

Rules of the game

- Each player takes a turn to roll the dice to see how many they will buy of each type of fruit. They then work out the total cost. For example:

Fruit	Price	Number to buy	Total cost
Plums	10p	3	30p

- At the end of the game, each player works out the total number of pieces of fruit bought, the total money spent and the change from £10.00. The player with the most change from £10.00 is the winner.

Fruit	Price	Number to buy	Total cost
Plums	10p		
Pears	20p		
Apples	30p		
Bananas	40p		
Oranges	50p		
	Totals		
	Change from £10.00		

Dear Helper,

This game is to help your child to work out the cost of buying multiple items, then find the total cost and the change from £10.00. If help is required, let your child use coins to work out the total costs, total spent and the change from £10.00. Challenge your child to work out the total cost if six of each type of fruit were bought, then to find the total number of items, the total cost of the fruit and the change from £10.00.

PHOTOCOPIABLE

Name:

Planning a picnic

Read these instructions with your Helper.

- Ask your Helper to plan some time for you to invite three friends to share a picnic with you.

- To prepare the picnic you will need:

  1 sliced loaf of bread
  Margarine
  Sandwich filling, for example
  cheese, ham, jam or
  savoury spread
  4 bags of crisps
  4 cartons of drink
  4 items of fruit or small cakes
  Kitchen foil or cling film
  4 plastic carrier bags

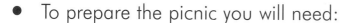

- Ask your Helper to take you to a shop to buy any items you need.

- Make up the picnic for each person as follows:

  1 round of sandwiches cut into quarters and wrapped in foil or cling film
  1 bag of crisps
  1 carton of drink
  1 piece of fruit or a small cake

- Place the items for each person in a plastic carrier bag.

- When you have finished the picnic, put all the litter in a bin.

Dear Helper,

This activity is to give your child a real-life experience of dividing items into quarters. When cutting the sandwiches, encourage them to recognise that four quarters equals one whole and that each will have a quarter share of the whole number of items. Challenge your child further by asking questions about the shared items, for example: *What fraction of four cakes will two children have?* Repeat the question for three children. Repeat the question for three sandwiches. IMPORTANT NOTE: If you plan for the children to go to a park for the picnic, you should accompany them.

Quartering a square puzzle

You will need: squared paper and four coloured pencils or felt-tipped pens.

Read these instructions with your Helper.

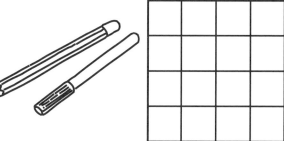

- Use four colours to colour four quarters in each grid. Find six different ways.

Clue: colour sets of four squares next to each other, for example:

- Try out ideas on squared paper before you copy them onto this sheet.

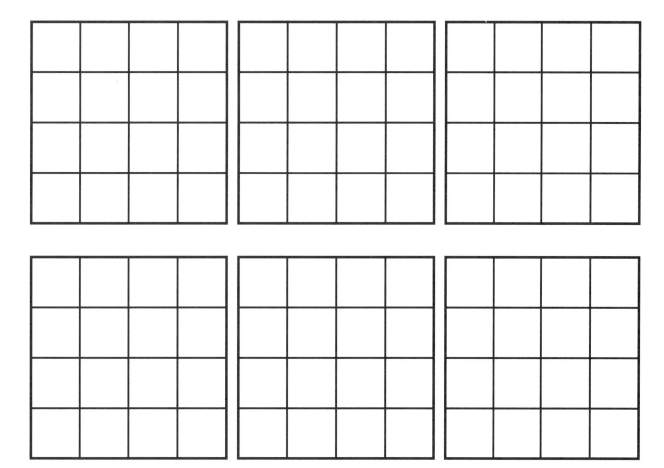

Dear Helper,

This puzzle is to help your child to recognise that squares can be cut into quarters in different ways. Guide them to look for ways to colour sets of four squares where each square touches the side of another square. An easier version: colour one quarter of each square differently in each grid (ie four squares in different positions). Challenge your child further by asking them to cut out the four coloured quarters of each square grid in turn, then to paste them back together as a whole square on a separate sheet.

Name:

How much time?

Read these instructions with your Helper.

- Write down the birthday dates of each member of your family on the chart. (Include grandparents, aunts, uncles or cousins if you wish).

- Colour in this month on the wheel above, then use the wheel to count how many months it is to the next birthday of each member of your family and write your results on the chart.

Name	Birthday	Months to person's next birthday

SOLVING PROBLEMS

NUMBER PROBLEMS IN MEASURES

Dear Helper,

This activity gives your child an opportunity to use their knowledge of the sequence of the months of the year to solve a real-life problem. Make the activity easier by scribing the difficult names of members of your family for your child. Let your child write the names of the months of each birthday. Encourage them to look at the wheel if help is required with spelling. Extend the activity by adding a fourth column to the chart and asking your child to work out how long it is to each birthday in weeks.

Travelling to London by train

Read these instructions with your Helper.

- Ask your Helper to help you plan an imaginary day trip to London on a Saturday.

- Use a telephone to ring the Trainline on **0845-748 4950** or visit the Trainline website on the internet at www.thetrainline.com

  Find out:

  - The times of two possible trains you could catch from your nearest station to a London station on a Saturday for your outward and return journeys.

  - The price of day-return fares for an adult and a child travelling on a Saturday from your nearest station to London.

- Together write down all the information you find in the table below.

Station to travel from	
Station in London	

Times of trains for the outward journey (morning).

	Depart	Arrive in London
Train 1		
Train 2		

Times of trains for the return journey (evening).

	Depart from London	Arrive
Train 1		
Train 2		

Prices of day-return fares to London.

	1st class	Standard	Saver	Apex	Other
Adult					
Child					

- With your Helper decide which trains you would catch and how much you would pay. Draw a tick beside the trains and fares you have chosen.

Dear Helper,

This activity gives your child the experience of finding out information needed to make a journey by train. It involves working with time and money and making decisions. If you are using a telephone, you may need to make the phone call for your child. If you are using the website, help your child to find the information on the screen. Point to the information needed for your child to write it down. Challenge your child further by asking: *What would be the total cost of the adult and child fares?*

SOLVING PROBLEMS

ORGANISING AND USING DATA

Mail sort

Read these instructions with your Helper.

- Keep a count of the different sorts of mail delivered to your house for one week, for example letters, parcels, bills, postcards, catalogues and junk mail.

- Complete the tally chart, drawing a tick for each item.

- At the end of the week count the total of each sort of mail and the total number of mail items delivered in one week.

Type of mail	Number of items ✓	Total in one week
	Total mail in one week	

Dear Helper,

This activity is to give your child a real-life experience of sorting and classifying mail and organising the information in a table. Discuss the results with your child in terms of the most/fewest items. To help your child find the total number of items delivered in one week, tell your child to count and draw a ring around sets of ten ticks, five ticks or two ticks in each row. Then to count up all the tens, followed by the fives, then the twos and any remaining ones. Extend the activity by asking your child to draw a graph of the results on squared paper, using one column for each type of mail and colouring one square for each item.

PHOTOCOPIABLE